363565

Contents

Pearson
PUBLISHING

Six Plays
that get shorter
and shorter

Brian McGuire

Brian McGuire is the head of a large Expressive Arts faculty. He has a great deal of experience as a consultant and senior examiner for drama. He is recognised as one of the country's leading authorities on drama.

Illustrations by Gary Hogg

Public performance notes

To prevent any infringement of copyright, if a school or college wishes to give a public performance of the plays, a licence must be obtained from Pearson Publishing.

A public performance constitutes a performance where any member of the public is present (for example, parents, VIPs). Performances given within the school with an audience of teachers of the school, pupils of the school or, in the case of examinations, an examiner are exempt from performance fees. Any performance where charges are made are subject to performance fees.

It is an infringement of the copyright to give any public performance or reading of the plays in their entirety or in the form of excerpts without prior consent in writing from the publisher. The plays are fully protected by copyright.

There are no performance fees applicable to the play *My Mother Says*.

All enquiries about performing rights, professional or amateur, should be directed to Pearson Publishing at the address below. Further copies of this publication may be obtained from:

Pearson Publishing
Chesterton Mill, French's Road, Cambridge CB4 3NP
Tel 01223 350555 Fax 01223 356484
Email info@pearson.co.uk   Web site http://www.pearson.co.uk/education/

ISBN: 1 85749 650 7
Published by Pearson Publishing 2000
© Pearson Publishing 2000
Plays © Brian McGuire 2000

Introduction

The plays contained in this book are ideal for drama, English and citizenship lessons at KS3 or KS4. They are suitable for:

- classroom reading
- performing in assemblies
- performing for open evenings
- practical drama/performing arts examinations
- public performance
- use as a resource for citizenship projects.

Play 1, *The Normalising Machine*, lasts 90 minutes and play 6, *My Mother Says*, lasts one minute, hence the title '*Six plays that get shorter and shorter*'!

The plays are very different, have been specially written for schools, and are great fun, both to read and to act.

Production notes, written exercises and humorous illustrations accompany the plays. Blank cue sheets are provided on pages 123 and 124 so that you can note your own lighting and sound plots.

Play details

Play 1 The Normalising Machine

Some time in the near future.:.

Despite various methods of reducing the male population having been implemented, there is still a lot of aggression in the world. Doctor Michael Molecule tries to create the Normalising Machine, a contraption that changes criminals into normal, 'nice' people. However, the task is beyond him. The final stages are completed by the sweet, young, innocent and extremely clever Grace Beverly Bryce. She even adds a finalising switch – which kills the criminal instead – to be used in emergencies only.

Citizens gain or lose citizenship points for the way they live. A lot of minus points means Judge Juniper Jones sends the 'unhealthy citizen' to be normalised. After normalising, the citizen is well behaved and, of course, criminals begin to disappear from society. Judge Juniper Jones and Grace Beverly Bryce rise to world recognition thanks to the public relations skills of Ben Percent. They also manage to make quite a lot of money. Everything is going well until it is noticed that normalising can wear off. Nevertheless, with the PR skills of Ben Percent, the devious mind of Judge Juniper Jones and the innocent looks of Grace Beverly Bryce, the trio manages to convince the world zones that finalising criminals is the best answer.

As time passes, finalising becomes a way of life or, more precisely, death. As more time passes, the population decreases even further. Good news for the unemployment figures but that's about all! It's almost science fiction. There's a moral but no happy ending. Even if there could be a happy ending, there would be very few citizens left to appreciate it!

The play is a modern comedy with a number of more serious undercurrents, ie power, greed, manipulation and the desire for fame.

Play 2 Coward

Kim is being bullied at school. She refuses to fight back. Her mother, her aunt and the headteacher offer her advice.

The play is suitable for use as a resource for a citizenship project or for supporting the school policy on bullying.

Play 3 Classroom Bullies

The classroom bully learns a lesson when the drama teacher organises a role-play on the theme of bullying.

The play is suitable for use as a resource for a citizenship project or for supporting the school policy on bullying.

Play 4 Happy Waiting Day

It's gran's 75th birthday. This is the future, so this will be gran's last birthday.

The play allows for thought-provoking and potentially moving performances.

Play 5 The Secret

Emma has a secret. She is desperate to share it with Mary.

The play provides an opportunity to practise comic acting, with timing being of particular importance.

Play 6 My Mother Says

A boy comes onstage to tell the audience what his mother says about him.

The play provides an opportunity to practise comic acting, with timing being of particular importance.

The Normalising Machine

This play is ideal as a school production, and can be as simple or as spectacular as you want. Advice on putting the show together is provided on page 8. It is also suitable for classroom reading at KS3/4.

- Amusing characters
- More parts for girls than boys
- Easy-to-organise set and costumes
- Specially created for schools

Cast list

Grace Beverly Bryce, Scientist
Ben Percent, PR agent
Judge Juniper Jones
Doctor Michael Molecule, Scientist
Siobhan Claire McKinnon, Reporter
Rudolf Fright
Anthony Badlad
Badlad's girlfriend
Trudie
Mr Tolerant, Trudie's dad
Mrs Tolerant, Trudie's mum
Minister for Education
Ms Heartless, Headteacher
Four narrators
Two newsrelaters
Two old ladies
Mrs Joinin
Seven zone representatives
Mum

Members of the cast also play:

Little girl
Little boy
Lady being robbed
Citizens of the court
Three criminals
Teachers
Teenagers
Four citizens shouting after Rudolph
A mother
Other citizens

Teacher
Small child
Special arrest squad
Nine citizens on trial
Pupils
Two female teenagers
Irate citizen
Eight-year-old boy
Lonely citizen

The characters

Grace Beverly Bryce: A sweet, innocent, clever, scientist who smiles a lot. She finishes the Normalising Machine. She's so naive she adds the finalising switch. The nearest she gets to justifying this deathly contraption is stating publicly that it should be used carefully. When you are dealing with Ben Percent and Judge Juniper Jones, that's a bit like saying to a couple of knife-wielding maniacs "Watch you don't cut something". Doesn't she realise what she has invented?

Ben Percent: Unscrupulous PR man who is simply after making lots of money for Grace, but even more for himself. He is an admirer of the zealous Judge Juniper Jones and it's not surprising he eventually wheedles his way into her affections. He has manipulated Grace Beverly Bryce but there is no chance of manipulating Judge Juniper. It's a pity we don't find out what a rotten life he will eventually lead under the thumb of Judge Juniper.

Judge Juniper Jones: Judge, enthusiastic orator and eventually world leader. Judge Juniper believes passionately that evil should be rooted out of society, no matter what it takes. She makes sure that the Normalising Machine helps her cause. When problems occur with the Normalising Machine, her answer is to use the finalising switch. It solves some problems but unfortunately a lot of the world's population disappears in the process.

Doctor Michael Molecule: Impatient and mad as a hatter, he is the first scientist to work on the Normalising Machine. He's clever but not clever enough to finish the machine, and certainly not clever enough to outwit Ben Percent – in fact, not clever enough to stay alive – a loser!

Siobhan Claire McKinnon, Reporter: Always in the thick of the action but eventually loses her job when Ben Percent and Judge Juniper Jones take over all the telewave stations. Losing her job makes her cry. She should think herself lucky; other people have been finalised. She should pick herself up and find another job. If she's articulate, she could apply to be a narrator.

Rudolf Fright: The first criminal to be normalised. As a criminal, he would bang your head against a wall. When normalised, he's so nice he drives you mad and makes you want to bang your own head against a wall. He even changes his name to Rudolf Right. When the normalising wears off, he becomes a criminal again but do we really want to see him finalised? It's tragic but crime doesn't pay unless you are Ben Percent, Judge Juniper or Grace Beverly Bryce.

Anthony Badlad: A criminal who is rotten through and through. He has a horrible, aggressive attitude, yet inexplicably has a girlfriend who loves him. It's a good job he's finalised in the first Act.

Badlad's girlfriend: She needs to think ahead. Fancy crying over someone like Anthony Badlad. Didn't his name suggest he would be trouble? It would also be helpful if she brought a mop and bucket to wipe up those floods of tears. Someone could slip on the wet floor.

Trudie: Girlfriend of Rudolf Fright. It doesn't always pay to give a criminal another chance. If you take up with bad company you get what you deserve. The whole episode has made her wary of boys.

Mr and Mrs Tolerant, Trudie's parents: They should be ashamed of themselves for letting their daughter go out with a criminal.

Minister for Education: She should think about speaking in plain English then we can all make sense of what she is saying. A bit sneaky, this minister… after all, she is the one who wants to finalise thousands of teenagers and we all know there's nothing wrong with teenagers.

Ms Heartless, Headteacher: The first headteacher to install a Normalising Machine in her school. She has a great dislike for pupils and loves nothing better than to create melodramatic poses to show how much she suffers because of them. She thinks the Normalising Machine is wonderful.

Narrators: At first, they seem like ordinary narrators filling in bits of the story here and there, but they also seem to help Judge Juniper and Ben Percent a lot. They are keen to stick anyone in the Normalising Machine without question. That's a bit worrying, but what is even more worrying is that they are prepared to shove people in to be finalised without question. After the takeover of the telewave stations, they become even more aggressive. At the end, they tell us how good the Finalising Machine is. This proves that narrators can sometimes be a bit naughty.

Newsrelaters: They do a good job to keep us informed of events as they unfold, but foolishly report untrue rumours. They don't move from their seats until the end of the play. Good parts for people who like sitting on their backsides and spouting. If they can't be bothered to move during the interval, send them a drink.

The two old ladies: Very old observers of the world but the nearest they get to anything remotely astute is their comment "It's marvellous what they can do these days."

Mrs Joinin: Who let her in?

Other parts: There are lots of other parts. Students can play criminals, mums, politicians, police, small children, nice children, naughty children, teenagers as we know them, ordinary citizens, irate citizens, lonely citizens, normalised citizens, naive citizens and dead citizens. Once offstage, students can resort to being themselves again. This may well be someone from the list of parts they have been playing, which just goes to show how the theatre can reflect real life.

Production notes

The main feature of the set is the Normalising Machine which is placed upstage centre. It should be large enough for someone to step inside. There is a hole in the front where the culprit's face can be seen. This will allow the audience to see the change from aggressive to placid personality. Lights surround the contraption. During the normalising process, sounds and flashing lights will add to the effect. During 'finalising', the effect created by the flashing lights and noises is more sinister. When a criminal comes out of the machine after being normalised, he/she will walk with a lighter gait and will continually smile. Above the set should be the words 'Some time in the near future'.

On stage left and right, there are large cut-outs which represent a type of television screen. These are used for the broadcasts from the newsrelaters. Newsrelaters can stay in position and the screens can be lit and blacked out as appropriate. The director may wish to consider setting microphones in the 'television booths' and adding a little echo to the newsrelaters' voices. When Ben Percent and Judge Juniper speak from the booths at the end of the play, the echo can be even more pronounced. When echo is needed, this is identified in the script by the symbol ◐ .The director, actors, sound and lighting technicians will find this symbol useful.

Music/sound effects can accompany various parts of the action. These are noted on pages 11 to 13. Some schools may decide to create their own incidental music.

The play is designed so that it is not necessary for the whole company to exit and enter. In many cases, the actors remain onstage. The cast can take on a variety of roles and the number in the cast can be expanded or reduced to suit needs. As well as the traditional role of narrating, the narrators also act as Judge Juniper's 'heavy gang'. The production requires more female roles than male.

A seat in the auditorium should be reserved for Mrs Joinin for each performance. She should be dressed as a member of the audience. She should take up her place before the show begins. Members of the audience should not be aware that she is a member of the cast. During Act Two, the actor playing Mrs Joinin can change costume and join the cast to take on a smaller part.

Costumes can be as elaborate or simple as desired, with perhaps the colour of the costume distinguishing the main and principal characters.

The characters are larger than life and should be played that way. Often, the actors can play parts of their speeches directly to the audience. The plot is sinister and much should be made of the melodramatic opportunities, particularly during the 'finalising' scenes. The production can be presented in as simple or as spectacular a way as you want. Whatever the approach, hopefully it will be fun to put together.

The running time is approximately 90 minutes.

Advice on casting

Many teachers will be pleased to note that this play needs a predominately female cast. Cast separate actors for all roles from Grace Beverly Bryce up to Mum (first section of the cast list). The principal roles are Ben Percent, Grace Beverly Bryce and Judge Juniper Jones. The other main roles are Siobhan Claire McKinnon, Newsrelaters 1 and 2, Narrators, Rudolf Fright, Trudie and Doctor Michael Molecule. Actors playing principal and main roles should not take on any other roles. For the other roles, there can be multiple casting. Anthony Badlad, Trudie's dad, Trudie's mum, Ms Heartless, Badlad's girlfriend and Mrs Joinin only appear in Act One. The Minister for Education appears in both acts but it is a small part and the actor could take on other minor roles.

Lighting

- Try to create a slightly sinister atmosphere for the opening sequence, perhaps using green or blue gels.

- Make the lighting on the Normalising Machine as spectacular as possible. During 'finalising', the lights should create a more eerie effect.

- When Siobhan Claire McKinnon is interviewing, lights can be dimmed on the cast and close lighting can be used on the interview.

- Use close lighting for the final dialogue at the end of Act One.

- Use flashing lights when Rudolf Right runs in (Act Two).

- Use close lighting on Siobhan when she is confronted by the narrators towards the end of Act Two.

Music links and sound effects

Act One

Page	Details	Link music/sound effects
14	Opening sequence.	Use music to suggest slow motion. This sequence can be up to two minutes long.
16	Exit of cast. Entrance of Grace and Ben.	Use same music as opening sequence.
18	Exit Grace and Ben. Enter Anthony Badlad.	Link music.
26	Revealing of the Normalising Machine.	Fanfare type music or snippets of *Hallelujah Chorus*, plus normalising sounds.
27	Rudolf enters the Normalising Machine.	Music to create tension prior to normalising, plus normalising sounds.
28	Rudolf and Trudie meet at the tube stop.	Lively link music.
29	Setting of scene: Mr and Mrs Tolerant's home.	Music as above.
32	Criminals enter the Normalising Machine.	Enough sound effects for three normalisings.
33	Anthony Badlad enters the Normalising Machine.	Louder than usual normalising sounds.
33	Anthony Badlad enters the Normalising Machine again.	Even louder normalising sounds.
34	Girlfriend pleads with Judge Juniper.	Perhaps a slow melody played on mandolin/violin or 'Hearts and flowers' on the piano. Music should create a very sad atmosphere.

Page	Details	Link music/sound effects
35	Mrs Joinin begins to share her thoughts with the audience.	Fade music out.
37	Anthony Badlad is finalised.	Sounds for the finalising, similar to normalising but more sinister.
37	Exit of cast.	Quiet music.
40	Enter pupils, teachers and headteacher.	Lively music.
41	Pupils go into the Normalising Machine.	Normalising sounds.
41	Exit headteacher, teachers and pupils.	Lively music.
42	End of Act One.	Normalising sounds, then lively music.

Act Two

Page	Details	Link music/sound effects
42	Opening sequence.	Pleasant-sounding music.
43	Citizens take places in courtroom.	Link music.
44	Teenager 1 ushered into the Normalising Machine.	Normalising sounds.
45	Teenager 2 pushed into the Normalising Machine.	Finalising sounds.
47	Exit of teenagers. Enter Judge Juniper and Ben Percent.	Lively link music.

Page	Details	Link music/sound effects
49	Crowd enters.	Link music.
51	Exit crowd.	Link music.
51	Irate citizen bundled into the Normalising Machine.	Normalising sounds but changing to finalising sounds.
52	Dr Michael Molecule enters the Normalising Machine.	Finalising sounds.
53	Rudolf Right runs in.	Alarm sounds.
55	Enter Judge Juniper and the narrators.	Menacing music.
57	Grace exits. Citizens pushed in a line.	Sinister music.
59	Exit of lonely citizen and Siobhan. Enter Judge Juniper and zone representatives.	Slightly sinister music.
62	End of Act Two.	Finalising sounds and lively music for bows.

The Normalising Machine

———— o ————

Some time in the near future...

Act 1

A large portable contraption with lights, wires, tubes, etc is centre stage. Members of the cast enter. They make their way to the acting area in slow motion. Suitable music plays. They are in pairs/groups. Each pair/group is enacting a crime. Various muggings are occurring, thieves are chased, etc. The narrators, the zone representatives, Doctor Michael Molecule and the newsrelaters enter. Doctor Michael Molecule stands by his invention. The action freezes and the first narrator speaks.

Narrator 1   At the turn of the millennium there was a nagging realisation that the natural aggressiveness of the world's population...

Narrator 2   ... and in particular of the male sex...

Narrator 1   ... would lead to the destruction of the world.

Narrator 4   A world summit with three representatives from the west...

The zone representatives identify themselves.

Zone 1   One

Zone 2   Two

Zone 3   Three

Narrator 4   ... three from the east...

Zone 4   Four

Zone 5   Five

Zone 6	Six
Narrator 4	… and one from Australia.
Zone 7	Hi! G'day, how are you? I'm representative number seven.
Narrator 4	… met to discuss how the world could be saved.
Zone 1	Medical science in zone one makes it possible to predict the sex of a child two days after conception.
Zone 4	In zone four, all breeding is artificially controlled so that there is a predominance of females.
Zone 3	Even with female dominance, there are still unacceptable levels of crime.
Zone 2	In zone two, a top scientist has been working on a brain-scanning machine that can eliminate aggressiveness. It can remove natural criminal tendencies and replace them with compassion, sensitivity and patience.

Doctor Michael Molecule breaks from the freeze. He is angry, upset; in fact, very wound up.

Doctor   The radicals should sedate the badicals and if we add… if we add… if we add… we add. We add what? What on Earth do we add? I cannot do it! Three years of my time and it doesn't work! It doesn't work! *(From angry, upset and wound up, his behaviour is now becoming berserk.)* It's no wonder my hair stands on end! There must be a way! There must be! There must be! There must be… but I can't find it! I'm a failure! I'm washed up. My life is down the tubes. It's not worth the flicker of an old bunsen burner. I'll have to resign before someone gets rid of me. I couldn't face all that awful publicity; and then there's the humiliation of it all.

He exits pushing his portable invention and still berating himself.

Zone 2   As I was saying, in zone two, a top scientist has been working on a brain-scanning machine that can eliminate aggressiveness. It can remove natural criminal tendencies and replace them with compassion, sensitivity and patience.

Zone 5	Are the tests complete?
Zone 2	I am almost certain they are.
Zone 3	You should be certain.
Zone 2	Like you, I am only a representative of my zone. Judge Juniper Jones is our leader.
Zone 7	What's the contraption called?
Zone 2	The Normalising Machine.
Zones 1, 3-7	The Normalising Machine. We want to hear more.
Zone 2	There will be further information on the news-screen very soon.
Zones 1, 3-7	How soon?

Everyone turns and faces newsrelater 1.

◑ **Newsrelater 1**	A representative from zone two has just informed the network that Grace Beverly Bryce, the youngest scientist to win the Peter Desmond prize for cranial study has taken over the final stages in the development of the Normalising Machine. The appointment was made by Judge Juniper Jones.

Exit all to appropriate music. Ben Percent enters and stands upstage. Enter Grace Beverly Bryce. She is talking to herself quite audibly.

Grace	If the radicals sedate the badicals... if the radicals sedate the badicals and we add *(becoming excited)* thermotriton heat, then scan for thirty seconds in each of the crevular nerves, that should be it! That's definitely right! I've done it! I've solved the final part of the experiment. The Normalising Machine will now operate. It's amazing how a short walk can clear the thought patterns. This could mean another prize for me. *(She sees Ben Percent.)* Did you hear what I was saying? I hope you didn't; it's top secret information. Are you familiar with my experiment? You're not press are you?

Ben	I'm not a reporter. How do you do? *(Putting out his hand to greet Grace.)* My name is Percent, Ben Percent, PR agent and you are Ms Grace Beverly Bryce. You should be careful with specialised information. A top secret could start a war.
Grace	Only if it's repeated.
Ben	*(Repeating Grace's words)* If the radicals sedate the badicals... if the radicals sedate the badicals and we add thermotriton heat, then scan for thirty seconds in each of the crevular nerves, that should be it! That's definitely right! I've done it! I've solved the final part of the experiment. The Normalising Machine will now operate. It's amazing how a short walk can clear the thought patterns. This could mean another prize for me. *(He pauses.)* You, Grace Beverly Bryce, will need advice from the right person, you need an agent. You've won prizes but are you rich?
Grace	I'm not interested in money, my true love is science.
Ben	I could make you rich.
Grace	When I won the Socrates prize at 15 I thought it was the greatest thrill of my life.
Ben	I could make you very rich.
Grace	When I won the Aristotle prize at 16 I could not begin to describe how I elated I felt. Then there was the Rousseau prize at 17...
Ben	I could make you very, very rich.
Grace	... but nothing has compared to winning the Peter Desmond prize. How rich?
Ben	The world is full of people who want to feather their own nests. Greed is a way of life; everybody wants a piece of the action. That's the way people are these days. You are young; you need the advice of an older, very experienced PR agent. If I looked after you, you wouldn't be taken for a ride. *(A little girl enters holding a chocolate bar.)* You see the trouble with the world today is that everyone is selfish, only interested in immediate gratification. *(As the girl*

Narrator 2	Bullied...
Anthony	*(To another small child)* And you, give me your dinner money!
Narrator 3	Spat...

Anthony Badlad spits.

Narrator 4	And truanted...
Anthony	I'm off!

He exits, almost knocking the narrators over.

Narrator 1	In fact, he spent his whole school career being, at best, obnoxious or vile.
Narrator 2	But there was worse to come.
Narrator 3	Theft...
Narrator 4	Arson...
Narrator 1	Fraud...
Narrator 2	Violence...
Narrator 3	Resisting arrest...
Narrator 4	And finally...
Narrators 1-3	And finally...
Narrator 4	I can't bring myself to say it.

All face newsrelater 2.

◀ Newsrelater 2	News just coming in is that an Anthony Badlad has eaten his mother and father. His only comment was that his father was more difficult to digest and tasted a little bit of urine.
All	Ugh!

All turn to face newsrelater 1.

It was confirmed today that Grace Beverly Bryce completed the Normalising Machine. Our reporter, Siobhan Claire McKinnon, is speaking to Grace and her agent at the moment.

Siobhan is interviewing Grace and Ben Percent.

Grace	The Normalising Machine scans the brain and can identify areas of weak moralistic attitudes. Just as there are areas of creativity or logic, there is a definite moralistic area. In simple terms, there are more bumps in this part of a criminal's brain than a law-abiding citizen's. By flattening these bumps, the criminal will have a better moralistic attitude. It's to do with the thermotriton heat.
Ben	This machine will change the destiny of mankind. It will redefine our very humanity. It will create a world of good people. *(Playing to an audience)* Now, what do I mean by good people? I mean people like you, people like me, people like us. People who believe in righteousness. Normal people who know how a true society should function. Grace Beverly Bryce has won many coveted prizes in her relatively short life but I predict by the end of the year she will be nominated for the Seven Zone Peace Award. By the way, this is the last free conference Ms Grace Beverly Bryce will be giving. All future interviews must be booked through me, Ben Percent, Ms Bryce's agent.
Siobhan	People are saying Anthony Badlad will be the first, erm… patient.
Ben	Ms Bryce can't comment on that.
Siobhan	This is Siobhan Claire McKinnon returning you to the news-screen.

Exit Siobhan. A lady rushes in chased by Anthony Badlad. The special arrest squad chases Anthony. He points his gun at the lady. She holds up her purse.

Lady	Here's my money. Please take it!
Anthony	I don't want your money. I want a hostage.

He throws the purse into the air. It is caught by Ben Percent who puts it in his pocket. The squad wield their firearms.

Squad	Freeze or we'll fire!
Ben	*(Creeping up behind and taking Anthony Badlad's gun)* You don't need to fire now. I think we have a candidate for the Normalising Machine here.

All face newsrelater 2.

◑ Newsrelater 2   Today in Telecaster High Street, Anthony Badlad was chased by members of the special arrest squad. Further details will be telewaved just as soon as the corporation has agreed broadcasting royalties with a Mr Ben Percent.

Citizens of the court sit around prior to the court session.

Narrator 1   All citizens in all zones collect or lose citizenship points.

Narrator 2   You can collect citizenship points for doing well in education or working hard.

Narrator 3   You can collect citizenship points for supporting the zone charities.

Narrator 4   But you can lose points for idleness, ignorance and crime.

Narrator 1   The citizenship scheme was initiated by Judge Juniper Jones.

The citizens begin talking.

Narrator 2   Silence for Judge Juniper Jones!

Narrator 3   Respect for Judge Juniper Jones!

Narrators   All rise for Judge Juniper Jones! *(The citizens stand and Judge Juniper enters.)* All sit! *(Citizens sit.)*

Judge   *(Addressing the court)* How does a human being live with an aggressive streak inside them? How does a human being suppress the potency of that anger? That's the important question of how a human being should live. Some will let that anger grow and fester until finally their evilness spits in the face of ordinary, decent people, and when they've spat you can bet your life some will spit again. They love the flavour of their evilness as it rolls around their mouth. They love how it manifests itself on the streets at night in muggings, arson and the despicable crimes of this millennium. And what do we, the good citizens of all zones, want? We want them to behave like us. We want them to be normal… and today you are going to see the first attempt of the normalising process. Today, you will see evil transformed into normality. Let me see you stand. *(The citizens stand.)* Let me see you sit. *(The citizens sit.)* Do you want to see the Normalising Machine? *(Some citizens mumble.)* Did you say yes? *(The citizens shout out "Yes!")* Let me see you stand again. *(The citizens stand.)* Let me hear you say "Evilness is wrong!" *(The citizens comply.)* Let me hear you believe it when you say it. *(The citizens repeat it.)* Let me hear it again. *(The citizens repeat it again.)* I want you to sit. *(They sit.)* I want you to stand. *(They stand. They comply with all requests.)* I want you to turn to your neighbour. I want you to shake them by the hand. I want you to say "Goodness will triumph." I want you to say it again. Say it louder! Sit down! Stand up! Stand on your head!

Citizens	What?
Judge	Sorry, I got carried away.
Narrator 1	Here are the citizens.

Enter more citizens, one at a time.

Judge	How many citizenship points?
Citizen 1	Plus 50 citizenship points.
Citizen 2	Plus 103 citizenship points.
Citizen 3	Plus 1027 citizenship points.
Citizen 4	Plus 1504 citizenship points.
Citizen 5	Plus 1742 citizenship points.
Judge	And you? *(pointing at Citizen 6)*
Citizen 6	Minus 4 citizenship points.

Citizens of the court emit a concerned murmur.

Citizen 7	Minus 25 citizenship points.

Citizens of the court emit a slightly louder concerned murmur.

| Citizen 8 | Minus 118 citizenship points. |

Citizens of the court emit even louder concerned murmurs.

| Citizen 9 | Minus 846 citizenship points. |

Citizens emit extremely loud murmurs of concern. Enter Rudolf Fright. He walks with attitude, looking disdainfully at all around him. He delights in declaring his minus citizen points.

| Rudolf | Minus 1327! |

Citizens emit deafening gasps of concern.

Rudolf	*(Defiantly)* And what are you going to do about it?
Judge	Move him to the left. Let him see what I am going to do. Let him see the unveiling of the Normalising Machine. Tell him he's going in it!
Narrators	You're going in it!
Rudolf	Oh no I'm not!
Judge	Tell him, oh yes he is!
Narrators	Oh yes you are!
Rudolf	Oh no I'm not!
Judge	Tell him to shut up!
Narrators	Shut up!
Judge	Tell him to sit down!
Narrators	Sit down!
Judge	Tell him to stand up!
Narrators	Stand up!
Judge	Tell him to sit down again!
Narrators	Sit down again!
Judge	Now tell him to watch!
Narrators	Watch!

The narrators force Rudolf to look. Music sounds and lights flash as the magnificent Normalising Machine is unveiled. Everyone is astounded. Standing on either side are Grace and Ben. A citizen becomes very overexcited. Judge Juniper puts her arm on the citizen's shoulder to steady her.

Judge   Be calm and live this moment of history.

Ben   To my right stands Grace Beverly Bryce, the woman who has given her heart to the completion of this Normalising Machine. The machine that will change civilisation forever.

Judge   *(Over-exuberant)* Grace Beverly Bryce is a saviour. Soon you will witness her moment of triumph as she turns the switch of the Normalising Machine *(pointing at Rudolf)* and you will emerge as a shining example of how perfect the undesirable can be made.

Rudolf   *(Standing and yelling back)* A machine won't change me!

Judge   Help him to the ground.

Rudolf is pushed to the floor by the narrators.

Ben   How many citizen points does the culprit have?

Rudolf   *(Leaping up and shouting aggressively)* Minus 1327!

He is pushed to the floor again by the narrators.

Ben   The worse the citizen, the bigger the dosage.

Grace   We'll only need to use switch one for this criminal.

Judge   Are you ready?

Grace and Ben Yes.

At the same time, Rudolf yells "Never!" He is thrust forward. The action freezes as the newsrelater speaks.

◀ **Newsrelater 1**   News is coming in that the first victim to enter the Normalising Machine will be Rudolf Fright, a criminal who has amassed minus 1327 citizenship points. We believe there have been some concerns raised by the Benevolent Society, who are opposed to experiments on live human beings. One moment… our reporter, Siobhan Claire McKinnon, is negotiating a fee with Mr Ben Percent and we should be able to telewave you there… now.

Ben Percent moves downstage to speak with Siobhan.

Siobhan   Is it true that no one has been in the Normalising Machine prior to Rudolf Fright?

Ben   Let me clarify the situation here. For the past few days Ms Bryce has experimented with a full troupe of monkeys in the Normalising Machine. These pre-trials have been stunningly successful. Within seconds of entering the machine, each monkey was acting in a most civilised way. They were no longer scratching or biting but were smiling and, as they came out of the machine, they began shaking each other by the paw. Very soon, some began putting on clothes, others set up tables and chairs, others picked up cups and saucers – in fact, the whole experiment ended up as a grand tea party. Thank you for your interest in the situation.

Siobhan   I would like to ask you one further question.

Ben   *(Interrupting)* In that case, I would need to discuss the fee for extending the interview.

Siobhan   This is Siobhan Claire McKinnon speaking to Ben Percent. Thank you and good afternoon.

Main lights come up on the action again and the freeze breaks.

Judge   *(To narrators)* Escort him to the machine.

Rudolf is thrust towards the steps up to the Normalising Machine. As he moves towards the machine, troubled music plays, and everyone points at the route Rudolf is to take. Rudolf is still defiant, calling out "I'll always be the same, I'll always be me!" Once inside the machine, his head sticks out through the hole, lights flash and weird sounds indicate that the process of normalisation has begun. Rudolf screams out "I hate you all!" Very soon, he is calm and smiling like someone who has eaten goodness for his breakfast.

Grace   He's ready.

Rudolf comes out of the Normalising Machine. As he makes his way downstage centre, he shakes the hands of and thanks Grace and Ben. Siobhan rushes forward.

Siobhan   Rudolf Fright, the whole seven zones are waiting for this. Tell us how do you feel?

Rudolf   I feel saved!

All face newsrelater 2.

◀ Newsrelater 2   It has been revealed today that Rudolf Fright, on the advice of his agent, Ben Percent, has changed his name to Rudolf Right. His behaviour is to be carefully monitored and, through the magic of telewave, we are able to bring you some of the more interesting moments.

A tube stop. Music plays and Trudie enters. She looks out for the tubebus. Enter Rudolf. His walk, his smile, in fact all his actions, are so gushingly nice. He is immediately captivated by the good looks of Trudie.

Rudolf   Hi! So you're waiting for a tube.

Trudie   Oh my gosh, you're that... that criminal.

Rudolf   Please, please, that was my past. Now I just want to be the nicest person you could ever meet. This nice person would like to meet *(pointing at Trudie)* this nice person. What do you say?

Trudie   I'm sorry but I hardly know you.

Rudolf   You have the most gorgeous eyes. *(He steps back.)* You are stunning. Absolutely beautiful.

His smile seems to stretch from one side of the acting area to the other.

Trudie   I suppose you have a cute smile.

Rudolf   I can see I am winning you over. I love the way you look. I love the way you talk. I love the very way you stand waiting for a tube. *(He goes to the other side of Trudie.)* And here you are, unprotected and so vulnerable. Let me look after you. Let me whisk you away from this. Can I call you a taxi?

Trudie	Oh, yes, that would be lovely.
Rudolf	You're a taxi. *(He laughs. He takes Trudie by the hand.)* Just a joke. We don't want transport. All we need is each other and maybe a beach to stroll along in the moonlight. Let me take you for a cherryade first.

Hand in hand, they exit. Two old ladies enter; they are carrying heavy bags. Rudolf enters as they speak.

Old lady 1	This bag is very heavy. If I could just rest for a moment.
Old lady 2	I would help you but I have this heavy bag as well.
Rudolf	Ladies, may I be of assistance?
Old lady 1	You're that... that criminal.
Old lady 2	Not now, they've changed him. He's been normalised.
Old lady 1	Ooh! It's marvellous what they can do these days.
Rudolf	May I help you with those bags? *(The bags are given to Rudolf. They are very, very heavy. Despite the strain caused by the weight, he keeps his smile.)* In which direction are we travelling?
Old lady 1	This way.
Old lady 2	She's 147 and she's still independent.
Rudolf	*(As they exit)* She looks very good for her age. In fact, you both look the picture of health. All that good living. It's a pleasure to spend time with such delightful citizens. You are an example to us all.

Mr and Mrs Tolerant, Trudie's mum and dad, enter. They take up positions in an area that represents their house. Mrs Tolerant looks out of an imaginary window. Mr Tolerant is dusting. Appropriate music plays.

Mr Tolerant	Who did you say Trudie was bringing home?
Mrs Tolerant	Her new boyfriend.
Mr Tolerant	What's his name?
Mrs Tolerant	Rudolf Right.
Mr Tolerant	The criminal?

Mrs Tolerant	He's not a criminal now, he's been normalised.
Mr Tolerant	Are you telling me you're happy for your daughter to go out with someone who's been normalised? Have you thought about the type of family he might come from?
Mrs Tolerant	Let's give him a chance.
Mr Tolerant	But what will people say?
Mrs Tolerant	Trudie thinks he's very nice.
Mr Tolerant	Yes, but will he stay normalised? Will we be able to trust him?

Trudie and Rudolf enter.

Trudie	Mum, dad. This is Rudolf.
Rudolf	I am very pleased to meet you Mr Tolerant. *(As Rudolf puts out his hand, Mr Tolerant squares up to him ready to fight but quickly realises he should be shaking hands.)* That's a good firm grip. It shows you have character. And is this Mrs Tolerant? You are Trudie's mum, aren't you? You could be taken for her sister. *(Mrs Tolerant is flattered. She giggles. Mr Tolerant is not impressed.)* What a lovely laugh. In fact, what a lovely couple. A lovely couple with a lovely daughter. A lovely daughter who is intelligent, thoughtful and completely gorgeous, and do you know what I find particularly attractive about Trudie? It's the way her soft golden hair tumbles onto her shoulders and her eyes shine like twinkling stars.
Mrs Tolerant	That's very nice Rudolf. You're making us feel embarrassed with all the compliments.
Rudolf	Oh, I'm so sorry. I didn't mean to make anyone feel embarrassed. Would you like me to leave? I do not want to cause any anxiety. Please forgive me. I am so sorry.
Mrs Tolerant	It's all right Rudolf.
Rudolf	*(He continues.)* No, no, no, I would not want anyone to feel the least bit uncomfortable because of me. Mr Tolerant, just tell me to leave this instant and I'll do it. *(Rudolf has a little moment of looking hurt but the big, big smile soon*

	returns.) I've been so rude, I haven't told you what a wonderful house you have. Those vases are perfect for this room, and that picture, only a connoisseur would have chosen that. Was that you, Mr Tolerant?
Mr Tolerant	Well, yes it was. I try to take a pride in the way the house looks. I do all my own decorating and cleaning.
Rudolf	This house smells.
Mr Tolerant	What?
Rudolf	This house smells of class. It's a credit to you. Yes, it really is.
Trudie	Should we go for our walk now?
Rudolf	Whenever you're ready, my sweetness. *(Shaking Mr Tolerant by the hand again)* Mr Tolerant, it's been a pleasure. *(He takes hold of Mrs Tolerant's hand and kisses it. She giggles again.)* And Mrs Tolerant, I do hope we meet again soon. *(He takes hold of Trudie's hand and they begin their exit.)* As we walk, I'll read you some of Shakespeare's sonnets. Don't worry, Mr and Mrs Tolerant, I'll make sure she's home by nine.
Mr and Mrs Tolerant	*(Waving goodbye)* Bye!

They look at each other.

Mrs Tolerant	So what do you think?
Mr Tolerant	A very observant young man.

All face newsrelater 1.

◀ **Newsrelater 1**	Today all citizens in zone 2 who have amassed more than minus 1000 citizenship points were lined up for the Normalising Machine. Our reporter, Siobhan Claire McKinnon, is speaking to the last batch.

Citizens are in a line for the Normalising Machine. They look and act aggressive. Ben Percent and Grace Beverly Bryce are in deep discussion. Judge Juniper is ready by the Normalising Machine.

Siobhan	How do you feel about becoming a normal citizen?
Criminal 1	*(Aggressively)* Sling your hook! Push off! Get yourself a proper job!
Siobhan	And you? Are you looking forward to being normalised?
Criminal 2	I'm not answering any stupid questions!
Siobhan	Perhaps this citizen will be a little more receptive.
Criminal 3	There's nothing wrong with me! Why am I here? I've done nothing! It's not my fault! Why me? I said, why me? What have I done?
Siobhan	Interesting, almost coherent, but unfortunately blatantly untrue. What about the gentleman at the end of the line?
Narrator 4	I wouldn't go anywhere near him. That's Anthony Badlad, they have a special dosage for him.
Narrators	Next!

One at a time, the criminals enter the Normalising Machine. Lights flash and weird noises sound. The procedure is quick. Each criminal comes out of the other side smiling and a normalised citizen. Each shakes hands with Ben Percent and Grace and takes a position downstage. Siobhan approaches the line.

Siobhan	How do you feel now?
All criminals	I feel saved!

They exit. Judge Juniper and Ben Percent move to centre stage. They shake hands. Narrator 3 explains to Siobhan.

Narrator 3	They have agreed on how to deal with Anthony Badlad.
Siobhan	Surely he's going in the Normalising Machine.
Judge	That's correct. Send him in!
Anthony	I don't want to go in!
Judge	Tell him to get in!
Narrators	Get in!
Anthony	This is not right!

Judge	Tell him it is!
Narrators	It is!
Anthony	It won't change me!
Judge	Tell him it will!
Narrators	It will!
Judge	Now stick him in!
Narrators	*(Pushing Anthony Badlad towards the machine)* Now get in!

Anthony Badlad enters the machine. There are louder noises and more flashing lights than in previous normalising. Despite the extra strong dosage, his face does not change to a smile. The machine can't seem to normalise him.

Judge	Get him out!
Narrators	Get out!

Anthony Badlad comes out leaping around the stage calling over and over "It hasn't worked!"

Judge	Sit him down!
Narrators	*(Thrusting Anthony Badlad to the floor)* Sit down!

Grace and Ben come downstage to meet the judge.

Grace	He will need a much bigger dosage.
Judge	Can you organise it?
Ben	She can, but remember the agreement. This will increase the cost.
Judge	Do it!
Grace	Send him in again.
Judge	Send him in again!
Narrators	In again!

Anthony is ushered into the machine.

Anthony	It won't work! She can't change me!

Again the normalising procedure begins. Despite a huge dosage, which causes the machine to shake, there is still no change to Anthony Badlad.

Judge　　He must be rotten through and through. Get him out again!

Narrators　　Out again!

Judge　　Ms Grace Beverly Bryce, what's the answer now?

Grace　　Obviously, he can't be normalised. It won't work.

Ben　　But the finalising switch will.

Judge　　Then try that.

Grace　　Do you know what that means?

Judge　　A bigger dosage?

Ben　　A different dosage.

Grace　　It means Anthony Badlad will be finalised.

Judge　　Do you mean he will be…?

Grace and Ben　　*(Nodding)* Yes.

Judge　　And I have the power to make that decision.

Grace　　You're the judge.

Judge　　Then the decision is made.

Ben　　You'll go down in history for this.

Judge　　*(To narrators)* Place him there!

Anthony Badlad is thrust on his knees to the side of the judge. Suddenly there is a cry from one of the onlookers; Anthony Badlad's girlfriend comes forward.

Girlfriend　　No! No! You can't finalise him. Please. Please, he's my boyfriend. I love him. To you he's a criminal but he's my reason for living. *(She gets down onto her knees.)* Please, I'm begging you, I'm begging you, judge, don't finalise him!

Anthony Badlad and his girlfriend are now looking at each other with deep affection.

Judge   The good of society comes first. Anthony Badlad, you will be the first criminal to be finalised. This is not a decision I make lightly. I have thought about it for well over, erm, twenty seconds and what must be done, must be done. It's *my* job to make great decisions and this is one of them. *(Heart-rending music plays and Anthony Badlad's girlfriend sobs uncontrollably.)* He will walk alone to the Normalising Machine.

Girlfriend   Please, please, please let me have a little time with him before he goes!

Judge   You have 45 seconds.

Girlfriend   *(Turning to Anthony Badlad. The music continues.)* Whatever you've done recently, it was wrong but I'll always remember when we first met. You were good then and we were right together. You fell in with the wrong kind, and maybe you have too many badicals in your brain but you're not the only criminal in the world. Why have they chosen you? *(She sobs uncontrollably again.)* I wish the machine could have cured you. I don't want to lose you. I know you love me and I want to be strong for you. *(Controlling her tears and forcing herself to be strong.)* When you enter that machine, hold your head up high and when they turn the control... *(It's too difficult to be strong.)* Goodbye my love, I'll think of you every moment for the rest of my life.

Again, she breaks down. By this time, all onlookers are in floods of tears. Slowly, Anthony Badlad begins the walk. After two steps, he faces the audience. The music alone makes you want to weep. He holds out his arms pleading for mercy. He wipes away tears. The onlookers emit a huge collective sob. Suddenly, a member of the audience, Mrs Joinin, is on her feet. The music fades. The cast are now watching the audience. Of course, the girlfriend is on her knees wiping away her tears.

Mrs Joinin   I can't sit here and listen to this! They are talking about death here. They are going to kill someone and you are all sitting watching! We can't let this happen. *(She makes her way along the first row of the audience.)* Excuse me, excuse me. *(Still in the audience)* Are you all going to sit here and watch that man die? *(She begins pointing at members of the audience.)* Are you? What about you?

Can you honestly let a man die before your very eyes? Can you live with that man's death? You must have some conscience! Well I'm afraid I'm not the sort of person who sits and watches something like this. *(She runs to Anthony Badlad and pulls him downstage.)* You poor, poor man. Let me speak to this judge.

Judge   Madam, you are making a scene. I would appreciate it if you...

Mrs Joinin   *(Cutting in)* Give me one brief moment to speak to you. Let the woman from the crowd talk to the judge about justice. No matter how we tamper with the mind of criminals we must always remember that there is never a simple answer. The Normalising Machine will not change the world for the better. There is a darkness about it. It's dark because it makes us forget the one single essential quality that makes us uniquely human. The quality of mercy, *(pause)* and it is not strained.

> "It droppeth as the gentle rain from heaven
> Upon the place beneath. It is twice blest:
> It blesseth him that gives and him that takes.
> 'Tis mightiest in the mightiest; it becomes
> The throned monarch better than his crown;
> His sceptre shows the force of temporal power,
> The attribute to awe and majesty,
> Wherein doth sit the dread and fear of kings;
> But mercy is above this sceptred sway,
> It is enthroned in the hearts of kings,
> It is... "

For a moment Mrs Joinin has turned her back on Anthony Badlad and he takes her purse from her pocket. She realises and is amazed.

Mrs Joinin   What!

Judge   He's taken your purse. Do you still want to be merciful?

Mrs Joinin   No, I do not. Stick him in the machine. *(She begins to exit.)* Some people can never be trusted, there's only one way to deal with them and that's to get rid of them, finalise them, and sort out the problem forever. *(She exits.)*

Judge   Anthony Badlad, your time is up.

Ben comes towards Anthony Badlad, takes the purse and pushes him in the direction of the Normalising Machine. Two of the narrators push Anthony Badlad into the machine, which begins the finalising process immediately. In this process, the noises are more sinister and the lights create an almost eerie effect. Very soon, Anthony Badlad's head bows forward in the hole.

The sounds and flashing lights stop, the music becomes very sad. Most of the cast exit slowly. Those remaining look at newsrelater 2.

◖ **Newsrelater 2**   Today Anthony Badlad became the first criminal to be finalised All zone representatives have met to discuss how each zone could have its own Normalising Machine. Ben Percent attended the meeting. At present, we are awaiting the outcome.

All look at newsrelater 1.

◖ **Newsrelater 1**   News is just coming in that Ben Percent has negotiated a deal with all zone representatives for the performing rights of the Normalising Machine. The training of the attached scientists and the construction of each machine will be overseen by Grace Beverly Bryce.

All look at newsrelater 2.

◖ **Newsrelater 2**   Further news reaching us is that Grace Beverly Bryce is expected to become a billion, billion, billionaire within two months. A beaming Ben Percent, Ms Bryce's agent, was keen to point out that the construction of these additional Normalising Machines will create employment in all zones.

The old ladies make their way to centre stage. Rudolf and Trudie approach.

Old lady 1   Ooh, look here's that nice man.

Old lady 2   He's with a girlfriend.

Old lady 1   They look as if they're in love. Hello young man.

Old lady 2   His name is Rudolf.

Old lady 1   Hello Rudolf. Is this your young lady?

Rudolf	May I say it's a pleasure to meet you both again and yes, this is my young lady, the dream of my life.
Old lady 2	He's such a lovely young man *(to Trudie)* and you are a very lucky girl.
Trudie	Yes, I think so.
Old lady 2	Ooh, she's lovely as well.
Old lady 1	If the world were full of people like you two and not that horrible Anthony Badlad, we wouldn't have to worry, would we?
Trudie	Anthony Badlad has been finalised.
Rudolf	It's a great shame, isn't it?
Old lady 1	Oh yes, but it's marvellous what they can do these days.

To link music, they all exit and the zone representatives take up positions.

Zone 1	In my zone, 50% of all known criminals have been normalised.
Zone 2	The Normalising Machine is changing the way of the world.
Zone 3	In my zone, the Normalising Machine has transformed life to almost perfection.
Zone 4	We have plans to build more machines.
Zone 5	In my zone, we have created more Normalising Machines than any other zone.
Zone 6	Tomorrow, for the first time in our zone, there will be a finalisation.
Zone 7	Your first one? In my zone, we've had 120!

Zone representatives 1 to 6 look at zone leader 7. She shrugs her shoulders. Exit zone leaders.

Ben Percent comes downstage with Anthony Badlad's girlfriend.

Ben	I can arrange full publication rights. There's a good story here... 'Decent young girl and the parent eater'. I can see the headlines... 'I gave him my heart but he had already

eaten two'. If we publish your autobiography we can write about your first meeting, how you got on with his parents, *(miming Anthony Badlad eating)* how he got on with his parents. Oh yes, we have plenty of material. There'll be documentaries, videos. You could make some money from this. Ninety percent of the money for you and a mere ten percent for me.

Girlfriend   *(Bewildered)* But I don't know what to do.

Ben   *(Producing a contract)* Just sign this contract.

Girlfriend   *(As they exit)* I'll have to think about it.

Ben   Don't think too long. Time is money.

Anyone onstage looks at newsrelater 1.

◑ Newsrelater 1   In zone two today, it was announced that a Normalising Machine would be installed in every school. The Minister for Education is with our correspondent, Siobhan Claire McKinnon.

Siobhan   Minister, the public is quite astounded at the idea of putting Normalising Machines in every school. After all, schools are places of education rather than correction.

Minister   First of all, may I say that the machines have only been installed in secondary schools. We realise that aggression is part of a child's make-up and we want to be realistic about the situation. However, many children are potential criminals. If, by secondary school age, they are still aggressive and are not in control of themselves, then the Normalising Machine will do its job and correct their behaviour. Nobody gets hurt and we are dealing with society's future problems.

Siobhan   But they are still children.

Minister   Let me ask you a question. Do you have children?

Siobhan   No.

Minister	Well I do and my little girl has been bullied at her secondary school. For weeks on end, she has come home in floods of tears, but tomorrow the bully will be put in the Normalising Machine and tomorrow night my daughter will come home with dry eyes.
Siobhan	Thank you, Minister.

Exit Siobhan and the minister. Music plays as pupils enter and stand in rows. The headteacher and a few other teachers take up their positions for a school assembly.

Headteacher	Good morning, pupils.
Pupils	Good morning, Ms Heartless.
Headteacher	We have a special assembly this morning. An assembly about goodness. An assembly about making sure pupils stay good. You will have heard the news about a Normalising Machine for each school, and ours stands behind me. Put your hand up if you think you are good. *(All pupils raise their hands.)* Interesting, mmm... some of you are *(pausing, then shouting)* little liars! For instance, you Samuel Sheldon, and you Chester Russell. Sit down! *(Ms Heartless's finger jabs the air pointing at various individuals.)* You, you, you, you, you, you, you, you, you and you are all trouble makers! Every single one of you has been a thorn in my side for the last two years. Ouch! Sharon Thatcher. Ouch! Gilbert Gough. Ouch! Raheesa Samad. *(She points at the others she indicated earlier.)* Ouch! Ouch! Ouch! Ouch! Ouch! Ouch! Ouch! Sit down! *(The targets sit down.)* How much do you think you can get away with? How much do you want me to take? There are some potential criminals in front of me. You, for instance, sit down! And then there's Martin Mindless, the year nine bully... well your bullying days are over. When I look at the smirks on your faces it angers me, but I am not going to wipe off the smirk, no, no, I'm going to change it to a big, big smile. I'm going to normalise you all. So you, you, you, you *(She carries on and points until all but one pupil has been identified.)* can sit down! The rest of the school is dismissed. *(The one child left standing looks*

round quite mystified. She turns back to the headteacher, curtseys and runs off.) Now let's have this machine switched on! *(Lights flash and the Normalising Machine sounds. Ms Heartless ushers several pupils towards the Normalising Machine.)* In, in, quick, quick! The staff will help you! *(The staff push, drag and poke pupils in the direction of the Normalising Machine. The normalising takes place very quickly. Pupils go in one side and, as they come out of the other side, smiling, they shake hands with Ms Heartless. After the handshake, they line up. The flashing lights and noise from the machine cease. Ms Heartless addresses the pupils.)* How do you feel?

Pupils   I feel saved.

Headteacher School dismissed.

To music, the pupils followed by the teachers then Ms Heartless exit. Judge Juniper, Grace Beverly Bryce and Ben Percent enter. They face directly out to the audience.

◑ Newsrelater 2 On last night's episode of *Face the People*, Judge Juniper Jones, Grace Beverly Bryce and Ben Percent made the following comments.

Judge   With the Normalising Machine in all secondary schools and with the predominance of females in the population, society is taking a turn for the better.

Ben   The Normalising Machine has become a part of the world's way of life, thanks to Ms Grace Beverly Bryce, the inventor.

Grace   Well, I wasn't the sole inventor.

Ben   Yes, but without you, there would not have been a Normalising Machine.

Grace   I can't take all the credit.

Ben   You can take ninety percent of it.

Judge   Well it doesn't matter who the inventor is, just as long as there are Normalising Machines everywhere.

Grace   *(Walking forward)* And just as long as they are used in a sensible way.

As Grace slowly exits, Ben and Judge Juniper follow her. The lights on the Normalising Machine flash, the noises begin. All lights fade, The lights and noises from the Normalising Machine eventually desist. Blackout. Houselights come on and lively music plays.

End of Act One

Act Two

To pleasant-sounding music, members of the cast enter as if they have all been normalised. They are smiling, they shake hands with each other, and they even shake hands with members of the audience. They ad lib pleasantries such as "It's nice to see you", "Isn't it a wonderful evening", "It's good to be alive", "You're looking very well", etc. The cast eventually make their way upstage. The music stops and the cast turn towards newsrelater 1.

◖ Newsrelater 1   Following the lead of zone 7, there has been a marked increase in the number of finalisations occurring in all zones. Grace Beverly Bryce, who recently celebrated her 19th birthday, is at present giving personal appearances in zones 1, 3 and 4. Personal appearances will take place in zones 5, 6 and 7 later in the year. In order to celebrate her birthday, Judge Juniper Jones has instigated hologram transmissions of Ms Bryce.

All turn to news-screen 2.

In news-screen 2, a still Grace Beverly Bryce can be seen. Ben Percent enters and stands centre stage.

Ben   *(Addressing the audience)* I've made Grace Beverly Bryce the most famous person in all seven zones and I've made myself a lot of money in the process.

Lights out on news-screen 2. All face newsrelater 1.

◖ Newsrelater 1   Thanks to our reporter, Siobhan Claire McKinnon, we can reveal some startling family background information about Grace Beverly Bryce. Her father, a genetic scientist, has been involved in several thefts of scientific dissertations.

Mr Bryce was normalised several weeks ago. Since the story broke, Grace Beverly Bryce has been out of the zone. This has led to rumours that she has stolen the idea of the Normalising Machine. For an unusually high fee, Ms McKinnon has managed another interview with Ben Percent, Ms Bryce's agent.

Lights on Ben and Siobhan. The citizens continue to look at newsrelater 1.

Siobhan   Can you clarify the situation regarding Grace Beverly Bryce's involvement with the development of the Normalising Machine?

Ben   It has been no secret that the initial work undertaken on the Normalising Machine was by another scientist.

Siobhan   Could I ask you the name of the scientist?

Ben   Doctor Michael Molecule. A clever young man but unfortunately not capable of the final and most important stages.

Siobhan   There have been suggestions that Grace Beverly Bryce stole the idea of the Normalising Machine.

Ben   Grace Beverly Bryce has not stolen anything! These rumours emanate from narrow-minded people who assume, because of a family background of theft, that purloining will continue in the next generation. Everywhere you look, there are holograms of Grace.

Again, Grace can be seen in news-screen 2. All citizens turn to news-screen 2.

Ben   *(Continuing)* Holograms to remind us of her greatness. Now I wish you good day.

He quickly exits. Siobhan, calling his name, chases after him. Grace disappears from news-screen 2 and is replaced by newsrelater 2. Link music plays. The citizens take their places ready for a courtroom scene. Judge Juniper enters.

Narrators   All rise for Judge Juniper Jones.

The citizens rise and the narrators push two female teenagers downstage left. The teenagers are guarded by the narrators. Trudie and Rudolf Right stand downstage right.

Narrators	All sit.
Judge	To my right is Rudolf Right. *(She walks towards Rudolf.)* Is that right?
Rudolf	That's right, Your Honour.
Judge	Right. *(To all)* Rudolf Right was the first person to be normalised. *(To Trudie)* Is that right?
Trudie	It's right, Your Honour.
Judge	And are you happy with Rudolf?
Trudie	I am, Your Honour.
Judge	Right, so here we have living proof of the success of the Normalising Machine. Right? *(No one responds. She repeats more forcibly.)* Right?
All	Right!
Judge	But to my *(stressing)* left are two female teenagers who have obviously left school and slipped through the net. I keep coming across female criminals. We have more females in our society now but that doesn't seem to be solving the crime problem. I'm waiting for someone to come up with some good ideas here. *(Annoyed by one teenager who can't keep still.)* Can't you stand still in a courtroom? *(To the calmer teenager)* How many citizenship points?
Teenager 1	Minus 250.
Judge	Normalise her.

The first teenager is ushered to the Normalising Machine by the narrators and the normalising process begins. At the same time, the second teenager elbows one of the narrators in the stomach. In retaliation, the teenager is flung to the ground and kicked once. Everyone in the courtroom gasps at the violence of the narrator. Everyone looks at the judge. The judge takes the narrator to one side.

Judge	You can't use violence like that. It's barbaric. *(She crosses to the teenager.)* How many citizenship points?
Teenager 2	*(Still in pain)* Minus 680.
Judge	Finalise her.
Teenager 2	What?

There are gasps from around the court.

Judge	*(Angry)* Finalise her! Get the first one out, put her in!
Teenager 2	What about my rights?
Judge	You've left your rights behind. Shove her in!

As teenager 1 comes out of the Normalising Machine, teenager 2 is pushed in for finalising. After the finalising and the disposal button is pressed, all continue to look upstage. At this point, all look at newsrelater 2.

◀ Newsrelater 2	The Minister for Education has just made the following proposal.
Minister	All teenagers irrespective of personality or attitude should be normalised. Those who are normal, once normalised, will still be normal; in fact, they will be even more affable. Those who are abnormal will become normal and if we can't normalise them then we should consider finalising them and save society any future anxieties.

All look at newsrelater 1.

◀ Newsrelater 1	She commented further that...
Minister	The normalising of all teenagers will begin next week.

She exits. The cast turns and faces downstage. They assume the roles of stereotypical teenagers. They are upset by the fact that they are to be normalised. Moaning, groaning, with exaggerated arm flinging and flopping, the teenagers let the audience know how they feel. Their astute comments are on the lines of:

Why do I have to be normalised?

Why is it always teenagers?

What have I done?

It wasn't my fault.

He hit me first.

Someone is always picking on me.

I'm tired.

I'm bored.

Why me?

It's not fair.

I can't be bothered.

Why do I have to do everything?

Everybody's got one.

The teenagers can make several comments each. Perhaps the comments could become 'a round'. When a mother makes her way to centre stage, the teenagers freeze. She rattles through her grievances.

Mum   You're lazy. You can't find anything to do. Your clothes are all over the floor. You eat us out of house and home. Your feet take up half of the lounge. You pick at parts of your body even when people are watching. You can't be civil. The most articulate sentence you've come out with in the last six months has been a grunt. You're always complaining. You're always telling me everyone else is better off than you. You sleep in your clothes. You take everything for granted. You've got grated cheese under your bed. You're selfish. You burp. You break wind. You only think about yourself. You don't do your Internet homework. You can't be bothered with anything. You never say please or thank you. Everywhere you go there's a mess. When did you last help around the house? When did you last tidy your bedroom? You embarrass me. I'm ashamed of you. I wish my life was as easy as yours. You smell!

At the end of the speech all the teenagers give a grunt and add the words "Yeah but," to the beginning of the comments they were making previously. Still moaning, groaning, flopping and flinging their arms, they

*exit to link music. Mum throws up her arms and gives a scream before
exiting. Ben Percent enters. He is approached by Judge Juniper.*

Judge   Ah, Ben Percent. I think it is time for a special award.

Ben   I don't need an award. As long as the money rolls in,
I'm happy.

Judge   The award is for me.

Ben   Oh. What did you have in mind?

Judge   The Grace Beverly Bryce Peace Award. It is only fitting that
a judge who has decided how man should live and a judge
who has created a better and safer society should be
recognised. I would like Grace Beverly Bryce to present the
award to me and I want you to organise it. Of course, there
will be a small financial reward for you.

The judge begins to exit but is met by Doctor Michael Molecule.

Doctor   Mr Ben Percent?

Judge   The busy man over there.

She indicates Ben Percent and exits.

Doctor   Mr Ben Percent?

Ben   I'm sorry, do I know you?

Doctor   If we had met earlier, you would be wanting ten percent
of me.

Ben   I'm not following you.

Doctor   I'm Doctor Michael Molecule. I was working on the
Normalising Machine... the one who was usurped. Without
me, you wouldn't be so stinking rich so I thought it would
only be fair if you organised some large payments for my
initial work.

Ben   You were paid by the zone government.

Doctor   I was, but you and Grace Beverly Bryce do seem to be
making a tidy sum. Don't you think I an entitled to a share?

Ben	No, I don't. You've only come forward when you think there is the possibility of money. You kept a low profile when Ms Bryce took over from you. That's because it didn't look good for you. The clever scientist couldn't do the job, but a young girl could. What I suggest you do is go away and try and invent something else.
Doctor	Well, that's exactly what I will do. I'll invent some rumours that will cause problems for you. I'll leave you to think about that. We'll meet again soon.

Exit Doctor Michael Molecule. Ben Percent moves upstage.

◑ Newsrelater 2	In a population census this week, it was revealed that, since the introduction of the Normalising Machine, there has been an overall population reduction of 30 percent. In zone seven, judges have changed the name of the Normalising Machine to the Finalising Machine. Ms Grace Beverly Bryce has become the first billion, billion, billion, billion, billionaire in zone two. The Minister for Education has now stated that…

Light out on news-screen 2 and lights on Minister for Education as she enters.

Minister	A better way of dealing with teenagers who accumulate minus 50 citizenship points would be to finalise them. I make this proposition because some of them don't normalise and suddenly we are dealing with criminals. If we cut straight to the finalising process, this would remove future criminals and have the advantage of decreasing the population. This would give us a stable, crime-free population whether it is predominantly male or female. New births can be monitored carefully. The monitoring would create another avenue of employment and, of course, my department would be prepared to oversee this.
◑ Newsrelater 2	Mr Ben Percent speaking on behalf of Judge Juniper Jones said…
Ben	I can see no difficulty in extending this scheme to all zones.

Link music plays. A crowd enters. Grace and Judge Juniper enter from upstage and join Ben Percent. Grace holds a trophy. The three of them take up prominent positions.

Ben   Citizens of zone two... today, Judge Juniper Jones receives the Grace Beverly Bryce Peace Award for her services to humanity. Judge Juniper Jones had the foresight to normalise and finalise the criminals of our society, making it safe for you to take public transport, walk the streets and go about your business without looking over your shoulders. This is a person who does not ponder while criminals smash and crumble our society. She makes decisions instantly, and that is something in which she takes pride. It is only fitting that Grace Beverly Bryce should make the presentation herself.

Grace   *(To the judge)* It is my pleasure to present you with the Grace Beverly Bryce Peace Award. Perhaps a few words would be appropriate.

Judge	Citizens, I am deeply honoured and moved by the kind words of Ben. There are people I must thank. I cannot take all the credit. Next to me stands Grace Beverly Bryce. Without her, I could not make great decisions because without her there would be no Normalising and Finalising Machine. I want to thank my parents… my father, who taught me that crime is an unnatural process, an evil that needs removing… then there is my dear mother who brought me up to respect the law and the leaders of our society who attempt to make a difference… and, finally, may I say thank you to every citizen who has believed in my judgement as I try to improve the moral quality of our lives.
Irate citizen	*(Calling out)* Who nominated you for the award and what about the rumours that Grace Beverly Bryce had minus 50 citizenship points when she began working on the Normalising Machine?
Ben	Where on earth has that rumour come from?
Irate citizen	The news-screen.

All look at news-screen 1.

◐ Newsrelater 1	We repeat our earlier newsflash. We have received information that Grace Beverly Bryce had accumulated minus 50 citizenship points when she began working on the Normalising Machine. At the moment, we cannot reveal our source.

Light out on news-screen 1. All look at news-screen 2.

◐ Newsrelater 2	We repeat the repeat of our earlier newsflash. We have received information that Grace Beverly Bryce had accumulated minus 50 citizenship points when she began working on the Normalising Machine. At the moment, we cannot reveal our source.

Light out on news-screen 2.

Ben	If that citizen would like to remain behind I will discuss the rumour with her. *(To the judge)* Leave me some help.

Ben talks to the narrators. The citizen with the question stands alone.

Judge Juniper and the other citizens exit. Siobhan Claire McKinnon interviews the two old ladies before exiting.

Siobhan   What do you think about the newsflash?

Old lady 2   It will be untrue.

Siobhan   Let's hope so. *(To old lady 1)* And what do you think about Judge Juniper receiving the Grace Beverly Bryce Peace Award?

Old lady 1   It's marvellous what they can do these days.

Link music plays. They exit. Ben Percent makes his way downstage.

Ben   *(To the narrators)* Put her in the Normalising Machine.

Despite protests, the narrators bundle the citizen into the Normalising Machine. The dial is set on normalising. The narrators press the switch and exit. Normalising begins. The citizen begins smiling. Ben walks to the machine and switches off the machine. The citizen continues to smile. Ben changes the dial to finalising and presses the switch. Very soon, the citizen's head flops forward. Ben pushes it back into the machine. He presses the disposal switch. Doctor Michael Molecule enters.

Doctor   Good afternoon, Mr Percent. I hope you are not having problems with the rumours about Grace Beverly Bryce. The one about her minus citizenship points is really unfair, isn't it?

Ben   I ought to beat you to pulp.

Doctor   Then you will have to be put in the Normalising Machine. There's another way of dealing with all this.

Ben   *(Thoughtful)* Yes. The disposal button.

Doctor   Another threat?

Ben   *(Thoughtful)* No. *(More thoughtful)* No. I'm going to make you a proposition. I can't deal with the rumours, so we have to reach some sort of agreement. What if I offer you the opportunity to return to the project?

Doctor   It would depend on the financial amount.

Ben	It will be substantial. Here's the problem. Before any bodies are emptied from the machine, they need to be instantly reduced to a small pile of dust. That way everything is a lot less messy. Do you think you could add that feature?
Doctor	That sounds possible. What exactly is the deal?
Ben	No more rumours from you and 50 percent of Grace Beverly Bryce's income for you from this moment.
Doctor	I think we are beginning to understand each other. So you want a modification to the disposal switch. *(As he considers the scientific problem, he makes his way to the Normalising Machine. To the delight of Ben Percent, it seems he is going to enter the machine but at the last moment steps back to look at the front of the machine. Each hesitation is a great disappointment for Ben Percent.)* If the thermotriton heat were stored in the machine after scanning the crevular nerves, and if we could direct this into a large loop system… I don't know… this is difficult… and it could depend on how much space there is in the control box… it may take up too much room.
Ben	This is your chance to be back on the project.
Doctor	Then let me look.

He enters the Normalising Machine. Ben runs to the machine and presses the switch.

Doctor Michael Molecule is finalised. His head drops forward. Ben laughs.

◖ Newsrelater 1	Judge Juniper Jones has declared that holograms of Ben Percent should be telewaved at regular intervals.
◖ Newsrelater 2	Ben Percent has declared that holograms of Judge Juniper Jones should be telewaved at regular intervals.

Enter Grace.

Grace	Oh my goodness, that's Doctor Michael Molecule. He's not a criminal.
Ben	Who do you think has been spreading the rumours about you? Well, he won't be creating any more.

Grace	Who finalised him?
Ben	I did.
Grace	Was that really necessary?
Ben	I did it to protect you.
Grace	But I don't want someone finalised. It's like the stories we read on the Internet about the Mafia.
Ben	You added the finalising switch to the machine.
Grace	But only to be used when the normalising procedure doesn't work.
Ben	There are a lot of exceptional circumstances these days. The only way we will achieve perfect lifestyles is if we root out evil.
Grace	You sound like Judge Jones.
Ben	Judge Juniper Jones is a woman to be admired.
Grace	We must ensure there are effective ways of controlling the finalising procedures. I must go and see Judge Jones.
Ben	She won't listen to you. You are a scientist not a policy maker.
Grace	And all you are is a PR agent.
Ben	Not any more. I am now the official first adviser for Judge Jones.
Grace	You can't finalise people at whim!

She exits.

Ben   *(Calling after her)* I did it to protect you!

He walks to the machine and thrusts the Doctor's head back into the machine.

Ben   Idiot.

He shakes his head and exits upstage. An alarm rings out. A scream is heard. Rudolf Right runs in. From an aisle in the auditorium, citizens shout after him. At the same time, the two old ladies, Siobhan and Trudie enter.

Citizen 1	Stop thief!
Citizen 2	He's taken my money!
Citizen 3	I thought he'd been normalised?
Citizen 4	Don't let him get away with it!
Citizen 1	The normalising hasn't worked!
Citizen 2	He needs to be sorted out!
Citizen 3	He's stolen my purse!
Citizens 1-4	Criminal!
Old lady 1	Hello Rudolf.
Rudolf	What's in the bag?
Old lady 2	Oh, nothing of importance.
Rudolf	Then I'll take it.

He snatches the bag; he laughs and runs off.

Old lady 2	He's a thief again.
Old lady 1	It's marvellous what they can't do these days.

They exit.

◖ **Newsrelater 1**	News is reaching us that Rudolf Right, the first criminal to be normalised, has changed his name back to Rudolf Fright and is once again involved in crime. Our reporter Siobhan Claire McKinnon is speaking to Trudie, his girlfriend.
Siobhan	Do you know why Rudolf has returned to his career in crime?
Trudie	This only happened yesterday. There seems to be no explanation. He suddenly became that criminal again. I thought I was the luckiest person in the world, but now I don't know what will happen. I'm hoping it's a temporary setback.
Siobhan	And if it's not?
Trudie	*(Upset)* Then the relationship is over.

Siobhan	This is Siobhan Claire McKinnon speaking to Trudie, almost ex-girlfriend of Rudolf Fright.

Trudie and Siobhan exit.

◖ Newsrelater 2	Rudolf Fright's particular situation is causing great concern across the zone. At the moment, Grace Beverly Bryce, Judge Juniper Jones and Ben Percent are not giving any interviews. However, a meeting of all seven zone representatives is being called. Judge Juniper Jones will preside over the proceedings.

To menacing music, Judge Juniper and the narrators enter. Judge Juniper addresses the narrators.

Judge	When Rudolf Fright is caught, he is to be finalised immediately. Is that understood?
Narrators	Yes, judge.
Judge	At the zone conference, I am going to suggest that any citizen who has attained minus 50 citizenship points should be finalised. I don't expect opposition. Now, begin making the arrests.

In a line across the stage, the narrators walk downstage to the audience. They hold a powergun each. They point them at the audience. Judge Juniper screams "Go!" The narrators exit. Grace enters.

Grace	Judge Juniper, I must speak to you.
Judge	Grace Beverly Bryce, the inventor of the Finalising Machine. I have great plans and I am sure you will be delighted to be involved.
Grace	I need to speak to you about who invented the *(stressing)* Normalising Machine. There has been an important development. The preliminary stages were completed by Doctor Michael Molecule and…
Judge	That may be so, but the credit for the Finalising Machine is yours. Citizens associate you with it. With your youth and that certain innocent look… you have the right image. It's good for my politics.

Grace	Something terrible has happened to Doctor Michael.
Judge	Then that's good news for us, especially if it puts an end to those dangerous rumours. If he undermines you then that could have a very adverse effect on how citizens view the Finalising Machine.
Grace	It's the *(stressing)* Normalising Machine. Why do you keep calling it the Finalising Machine?
Judge	What exactly do you want me to do about Doctor Michael Molecule?
Grace	I'm trying to tell you that Ben Percent has already dealt with him. He's used the Finalising, I mean, the *(stressing)* Normalising Machine.
Judge	Has the doctor been finalised or normalised?
Grace	He's been finalised.
Judge	Then that's a problem solved.
Grace	Finalising citizens isn't the answer to everything. There are other ways of dealing with crime.
Judge	So you think Doctor Michael is a criminal.
Grace	No. He's made a mistake. He probably felt he was entitled to more recognition for his work. We can't really blame him for being upset.
Judge	Let me remind you about minus citizenship points. Citizens can lose points for ignorance. I think, in this case, Doctor Michael Molecule has lost a considerable amount and we certainly don't want him associated with the Finalising Machine.
Grace	I don't think you are listening to me. He's been killed.
Judge	Finalised.
Grace	Finalised, killed. You can give it whatever name you want. It's still death.
Judge	You finished the machine. You added the finalising switch.
Grace	It was put there to act as a warning or for extreme cases.

| **Judge** | Any criminal is in an extreme case. Their minds work differently to ordinary citizens. The normalising process isn't effective but finalising will remove the unacceptable element and will be a deterrent for anyone considering crime. Citizens from all zones know who you are. They all know what you have invented. There's only one way forward now. |

Sinister music plays as Grace runs off. Screams are heard. A number of citizens including Rudolf Fright and a little boy are pushed into a line downstage by the narrators.

| **Judge** | Make them kneel. |
| **Narrators** | Kneel! |

The citizens are pushed in the back by the narrators' powerguns. They are forced to kneel. The little boy sobs.

Judge	What is that wailing?
Citizen	*(Standing up)* He's only a little boy.
Judge	He's a criminal and he's under arrest.
Citizen	He doesn't understand what is going on.
Judge	He understood how to lie, steal and cheat the world so, like everyone else here, he'll be finalised.
Citizen	*(Coming forward)* He's only eight!
Judge	Get her back in line! *(The narrators push the citizen back to her knees.)* We'll begin with Rudolf Fright.
Rudolf	If the machine couldn't normalise me, then it probably won't be able to finalise me!
Judge	Then watch me prove you wrong. Get him in!
Narrators	In!

Using the butts of their guns, two of the narrators push Rudolf towards the machine. Rudolf enters the machine. Again, the little boy cries.

| **Judge** | And he's next! |

◑ Newsrelater 1   Yesterday, there was pandemonium at the finalising of
Rudolf Fright.

*Other citizens run in. The arrested citizens try to escape. The narrators try
to quell the riot. All freeze.*

◑ Newsrelater 2   A mother tried to rescue her son from finalising.

*Again, everyone runs round. The mother grabs her son by his arm, a
narrator grabs the other arm. All freeze.*

◑ Newsrelater 1   Citizens ran screaming through the streets.

*Citizens run downstage. They raise their hands in surrender. The narrators
point the powerguns at the citizens. All freeze.*

◑ Newsrelater 1   Eventually everyone was arrested. All culprits were finalised.

Newsrelater 2   Even the little boy?

Newsrelater 1   *(Sadly)* Even the little boy.

Blackout apart from lights around the Normalising Machine. Rudolf Fright screams as he is finalised. Lights out and light on newsrelater.

Newsrelater 2   Our reporter, Siobhan Claire McKinnon, gives us an update of the ordinary citizens' opinions on the recent finalisings.

Siobhan runs in.

Siobhan   What do you want me to do?

**Newsrelaters
1 and 2**   Interview someone.

Siobhan   There's no one here. *(A citizen enters.)* Ah, wait a moment. Excuse me madam, may I interview you?

Lonely citizen   *(Excitedly)* Definitely! Definitely! You can, definitely.

Siobhan   Can I ask you…

Lonely citizen   *(Cutting in before the question is finished)* I would like to say that there was me, Kirsty, Katherine, Kelly, Katy, Kristian, Kyle, Krypton, Kerrie, Katrina, Jodie, Jacqueline, Jonathan, Jazel, Joanne and Jessica. Last week, Kirsty, Katherine, Kelly, Katy, Kristian, Kyle, Krypton, Kerrie and Katrina were finalised. Yesterday, Jodie, Jacqueline, Jonathan, Jazel, Joanne and Jessica were finalised. Now I'm on my own.

Siobhan   Is there anything else you would like to say?

Lonely citizen   Yes, will you be my friend?

To music, they exit. Judge Juniper and the zone representatives enter.

Judge   We cannot make any sort of retreat. All criminals must be dealt with and our procedures should be alike. If the normalising process is problematic, then we need to make a stronger case for finalising.

Zone 2   Perhaps the normalising process could be rectified.

Judge	Maybe it could, but is that what we all want? The finalising process works every time.
Zone 7	There are certainly no problems in my zone.
Zone 4	Do Finalising Machines deal effectively with crime?
Zone 7	We are fully committed to finalising.
Judge	Perhaps you would like to share some of the arguments you put to the citizens in your zone to help them realise the importance of finalising.
Zone 7	Finalising keeps criminals at bay because their numbers are immediately reduced. This means they cannot learn from each other. More importantly, they fear finalising and it makes them steer clear of crime. All citizens want safety. In my zone, it is every normal citizen's right. Our slogan is 'We guarantee safety'. We are now finalising fewer criminals. For us, the system has worked.
Zone 5	But your population has reduced dramatically.
Zone 7	So has our unemployment, tube rage, road rage, air rage, sea rage. In fact, zone 7 boasts a highly sensitive citizenship.
Judge	I think zone 7 has given us the arguments we need. All we need to agree is the number of minus citizenship points for finalisation. I am going to suggest 50. Agreed?
Zones 1-7	Agreed.

The zone leaders face upstage.

Judge	Of course, there is the media to deal with.

The judge moves upstage. Siobhan Claire McKinnon runs in. From either side, the narrators run in. Each pair blocks the path of Siobhan. They are menacing as they speak. As this occurs, Grace enters upstage. Newsrelater 1 and 2 slowly leave their places behind the screens and begin to walk downstage. Ben Percent and Judge Juniper Jones take up positions in the news-screens.

Narrator 1	All information to be telewaved will be checked.
Narrator 2	All information to be telewaved will be double-checked.

Narrator 3	All information to be telewaved is subject to scrutiny.
Narrator 4	All future information will be relevant to how the zones are organised.
Narrator 1	The copyright of all future information is the property of Ben Percent and Judge Juniper Jones.
All narrators	All future information will be of vital importance.
◖ Newsrelater 1	Today, all stations were taken over by Judge Juniper Jones and Ben Percent on behalf of the seven world zones.
◖ Newsrelater 2	Our final news bulletin was to relay information about the engagement of Ben Percent and Judge Juniper Jones. However, this information will not now be telewaved.
◖ Newsrelaters 1 and 2	Our reporter, Siobhan Claire McKinnon, said…
Siobhan	I am unemployed!

Ben Percent appears in news-screen 1. All look at news-screen 1.

| **◖ Ben** | I am proud to be wealthy and successful, but more than anything else, I am proud to be associated with the promotion of the Finalising Machine. |

Light out on news-screen 1. Judge Juniper Jones appears in news-screen 2. All look at news-screen 2.

| **◖ Judge** | I have achieved fame and power, but history will recall how my great decisions have changed all zones for the better. |

Light out on news-screen 2. The narrators move forward.

Narrator 1	No crime.
Narrator 2	No injustice.
Narrator 3	No worries.
All narrators	You are now living in a perfect world.
Narrators and zones 1–7	Thanks to the Finalising Machine.

Grace comes through the narrators to take a downstage centre position.
All look at her.

Grace   Just as long as it is used in a sensible way.

All face the flashing lights of the Finalising Machine. Its eerie finalising
sounds are heard. The rest of the cast enter to gaze at the machine. The
lights fade on the cast then the whole stage is blacked out. The lights
come up. Lively music plays and the cast take their bow. They exit. Music
and lights fade.

Worksheet on *The Normalising Machine*

Questions

1 Which prizes did Grace Beverly Bryce win?

....

2 Name three people for whom Ben Percent acted as an agent.

....

3 Name some of Anthony Badlad's crimes.

....

4 In which street was Anthony Badlad chased by members of the special arrest squad?

....

5 How do people gain citizenship points?

....

6 How do people lose citizenship points?

....

7 What is the full name of Rudolf Fright's girlfriend?

....

8 Who is the first criminal to be normalised, and how many minus citizenship points did he amass?

....

9 Who is the first criminal to be finalised?

....

10 Why does Mrs Joinin change her mind about saving Anthony Badlad from being finalised?

....

11 Why does the Minister for Education think it is a good idea to install Normalising Machines in schools?

....

12 Which zone has the greatest number of finalisings?

....

13 Which zone changes the name of the Normalising Machine to the Finalising Machine?

....

14 Which award does Judge Juniper Jones receive and whose idea is it that she should be presented with it?

....

....

15 How does Ben Percent trick Doctor Michael Molecule into entering the Finalising Machine?

....

....

Research

In which play does the 'Quality of mercy' speech originally appear? Who said it? Can you also name the author?

Name of speaker: ....

Name of play: ....

Author of play: ....

Advice to the actors

What advice would you give to someone playing the part of:

Ben Percent ....

....

....

....

....

....

Grace Beverly Bryce ....

....

....

....

....

Judge Juniper Jones ....

....

....

....

....

A character of your choice ....

....

....

....

....

Coward

The play is suitable for:

- drama/performing arts examination performances
- workshop presentations
- classroom reading for KS4.

Cast list

Kim Marshall, aged 15
Mrs Marshall, Kim's mother
Sarah Lee, Kim's aunt
Mr Wilson, Headteacher
Joanne Morton
Mr Morton, Joanne's father
Girl 1
Girl 2
Woman 1
Woman 2

Production notes

With doubling up, the play can be presented by six players. By changing the names, roles can be male or female. The sets can be as simple as a couple of chairs or a settee. Few properties are needed.

The stage direction 'Lights out' is to show the end of a particular sequence, although it is not necessary for the actors to leave the acting area as the action may return there almost immediately. Instead of dimming the lights, actors may hold freeze positions when in the acting area and not in the action.

Pages 68 and 69 show the basics of the lighting plot.

The running time is approximately 30 minutes.

Lighting cue sheet

Page	Cue	Lighting
71	Kim: I don't want to go to school.	Lights out on Sarah. Lights up on Kim's mum and Kim.
72	Mrs Marshall: Sometimes I wonder if I'm going to cope.	Lights out on Mrs Marshall. Lights up on Kim and Sarah.
72	Kim: I don't want to go to school because of Joanne Morton.	Lights out on Kim and Sarah. Lights up on Joanne and Mr Morton.
73	Mr Morton: Get it for me!	Lights out on Joanne and Mr Morton. Lights up on Kim and Sarah.
74	Kim: She hasn't any time to listen to me, never mind help me.	Lights out on Kim and Sarah. Lights up on Joanne and Mr Morton.
74	Mr Morton: You need to be the same.	Lights out on Joanne and Mr Morton. Lights up on Kim and Sarah.
75	Kim: All I want is to be left alone.	Lights out on Kim and Sarah. Lights up on Joanne and Mr Morton.
75	Mr Morton: You're learning.	Lights out on Joanne and Mr Morton. Lights up on Kim and Sarah.
75	Kim: I think I know what I'm going to do.	Lights out on Kim and Sarah. Lights up on two women and Mr Morton.
76	Mr Morton: I've already knocked your husband out.	Lights out on two women. Lights kept on Mr Morton.
76	Mr Morton: Don't try anything like that again.	Lights out on Joanne and Mr Morton. Lights up on Kim and Sarah.
77	Sarah: Then it's worth trying. End of Scene 1.	Lights out. Lights up for Scene 2.

Page	Cue	Lighting
78	Joanne: Coward! End of Scene 2.	Lights out. Lights up for Scene 3.
81	Mr Wilson: We don't want to involve the educational welfare officer, do we?	Lights out on Mr Wilson, Kim and Sarah. Lights up on Mrs Marshall.
81	Mrs Marshall: These are the details.	Lights out on Mrs Marshall. Lights up on Mrs Marshall and Kim.
81	Mrs Marshall: Not now, Kim. My head is spinning. End of Scene 3.	Lights out. Lights up for Scene 4.
82	Joanne: See what will happen. (Girls kick Kim.)	Lights out on Joanne, Kim and two girls. Lights up on Mrs Marshall.
82	Mrs Marshall: Why should I be put in this situation when I haven't done anything wrong? End of Scene 4.	Lights out. Lights up for Scene 5.
83	Mr Wilson: I don't think you need to worry about Joanne Morton any more. End of Scene 5.	Lights out. Lights up for Scene 6.
84	Mrs Marshall: What about the three of us going out for a meal? End of Scene 6.	Lights out. Lights up for Scene 7.
85	Mr Wilson: I think we've all learned something from this. End of Scene 7.	Lights out.

Coward

—— ○ ——

Scene 1: Sarah's house

A cup of tea is on the floor. Kim stands, Sarah sits. Kim is obviously upset. She does not respond to Sarah's questions.

Sarah   I can't do anything if you won't tell me. What's wrong with you? Is it your dad? Is it your mum? Have you fallen out with Andrea again? I'm trying to help you. *(She picks up the teacup and passes it to Kim.)* Drink your tea. *(Kim takes one sip and puts the teacup back on the floor. Sarah sits again.)* Shall I leave you for a while? You can tell me when you're ready. Is it some sort of trouble with a boy? *(Kim looks at Sarah.)* Oh Kim, it's not, is it? You better tell me what's happened.

Kim   It isn't boy trouble.

Sarah   Then what is it?

Kim   School.

Sarah   Are you falling behind with your work?

Kim   No. Well, a couple of lessons.

Sarah   You've always done so well at school. You've had a lot to live up to following Andrea but I think you're going to do better than her. I shouldn't say that but I think you've always been brighter. You have a good command of language. You won't let the family down. Andrea's a teacher and we're pleased with that, but you, you'll go further. I'm going to be proud of my favourite niece.

Kim   It's not the work. I can catch up if I want to. I'm not that far behind.

Sarah	Are you finding the work difficult? You've never had problems before.
Kim	*(Stronger)* I don't want to go to school.

Lights out on Sarah. Kim walks across stage. Her mum sits on a chair. She is upset. Kim stands behind her. She puts her hand on her mum's shoulder. Kim's mum holds up a letter.

Mrs Marshall	I've been expecting this for months. Do you want to read it?

Kim takes the letter and reads.

Kim	This isn't fair. It's not right. Because you prevented someone from being hurt, there's the possibility of you losing your job. What sort of people are these? *(She glances at the letter again.)* And they want you to appear before a tribunal to defend yourself.
Mrs Marshall	At the moment the tribunal is taking the view that I injured someone, and if the story is twisted the wrong way, that will be bad publicity for Somerdales. I've seen it happen before. Businesses can't take chances these days.
Kim	A boy attacks another boy in the shop, you pull him back. That, to anyone with any sense, is the right thing to do. In fact, I would say it was brave. Yet at the moment you seem to be in the wrong.
Mrs Marshall	I sprained his wrist.
Kim	If he'd had his wrists slapped at home now and again maybe he wouldn't have made a blatant attack on someone. It's stupid; there isn't anything to worry about.
Mrs Marshall	I'll lose my job.
Kim	They wouldn't do that.
Mrs Marshall	I'll be the scapegoat. It will save them a lot of trouble.
Kim	You'll be able to stand up to the tribunal. Have you asked dad what he thinks?
Mrs Marshall	Your father is not here!
Kim	It's not his fault.

| Kim | I see her for ten minutes in the morning. That's if we don't have an assembly. She's always giving out raffle tickets, sponsor forms and then there are the announcements. She hasn't any time to listen to me, never mind help me. |

Lights out on Kim and Sarah. Lights up on Joanne and Mr Morton. Joanne is cowering. Her father stands over her. He is threatening to hit her.

Mr Morton	Fourteen years old and you can't sort out those kids!
Joanne	Dad! Dad! Please! Please! I don't want to!
Mr Morton	You're soft. You're like your mother. *(Taking hold of Joanne)* You don't let those kids in the street push you around. Now get back out there and sort it out! *(Pushing Joanne away)* You fight, Joanne. You fight to get what you want! Some of those kids are younger than you. You sort them, don't let them get the better of you. People are frightened of me and that gets me respect. You need to be the same.

Lights out on Joanne and Mr Morton. Lights up on Kim and Sarah.

Sarah	What about your exams?
Kim	Are they more important than my self-respect or even my sanity?
Sarah	Why does she pick on you?
Kim	Because I won't fight back.
Sarah	And could you? Are you saying, you could fight back but you don't want to?
Kim	*(Sitting)* I won't fight.
Sarah	You know, when I was at Oakwood, a girl kept picking on me. She wasn't much bigger but she made the first year unbearable. One lunchtime in the geography room, we both had to finish some work. When the teacher left, she was straight over to my desk asking for money and trying to drag me from my seat. I don't know what it was but I'd had enough. I flung her against the metal frame of the window, the one that protects the blinds. She wasn't expecting it. I mean, she had been getting away with it all year. I threw her

so hard she buckled the frame and hurt her back. Then she started to cry. *(Sitting)* That's all it took. She never bothered me again. She had picked on me because she thought I was weaker. I wasn't, I just hadn't fought back. Have you thought about standing up to this Joanne Morton?

Kim   All I want is to be left alone.

Lights out on Kim and Sarah. Lights up on Joanne and Mr Morton.

Mr Morton   *(Holding out his hand)* Here.

Joanne   What?

Mr Morton   Here!

Joanne   What's this for?

Mr Morton   Because you're getting to be a good fighter.

Joanne   *(Taking the money)* Five pounds.

Mr Morton   You're taking after your dad not your mother. You're learning.

Lights out on Joanne and Mr Morton. Lights up on Kim and Sarah.

Sarah   What about going to see the parents of some of this girl's friends? Without her friends supporting her, she might leave you alone.

Kim   It's not easy breaking up gangs. *(Pause)* I think I know what I'm going to do.

Lights out on Kim and Sarah. Lights up on two women and Mr Morton.

Woman 1   Hey! Billy Morton! Your Joanne's been picking on our Danielle again. You better do something about it.

Mr Morton   She deserved it.

Woman 2   Your Joanne's always fighting these days. She's like an animal. You Mortons are the talk of the estate. She needs a mother, your Joanne.

Woman 1   She should be locked up.

Mr Morton   Mind your own business or you'll get a fist in the face. I've already knocked your husband out.

Lights out on Woman 1 and Woman 2. Joanne rushes in. Mr Morton attempts to grab hold of her.

Mr Morton   Where are you going?

Joanne   *(Shrugging off Mr Morton)* To my room.

Mr Morton   What have you got in your hand?

Joanne   Nothing.

Mr Morton   *(Taking hold of Joanne's wrist)* Open it!

Joanne   You're hurting me!

Mr Morton   Then open your hand! *(Joanne opens her hand to reveal some money.)* Where did you get that?

Joanne   I've taken it from people.

Mr Morton   Then I'll have some of it. *(He takes the money.)*

Joanne   Give it back to me! *(She snatches at Mr Morton's hand but he moves it.)*

Mr Morton   Not quick enough. *(Joanne sinks her teeth into his other hand.)* Ow! You little cow! *(He flings her to the ground.)* Don't try anything like that again.

Lights out on Joanne and Mr Morton. Lights up on Kim and Sarah.

Kim   I'm going to write down a plan for the school that will protect people like me from bullies. I'm going to show ways of educating Joanne Morton and her friends to some sort of normal behaviour. They need to see how wrong they are and how people feel when they hurt them. I have plenty ideas. When I've written it up, I'll take it to Mr Wilson.

Sarah   Why don't we go to Joanne Morton's house and talk to her parents?

Kim   Parent. There's only her father. And he frequently beats her up as well as other people on the estate. I'm not after a gang war.

Sarah	Do you think Mr Wilson will take notice of your ideas?
Kim	If he doesn't then I'll continue to get beaten up.
Sarah	Then it's worth trying.

Lights out.

Scene 2: School

Joanne Morton and two friends approach Kim. They block her path.

Joanne	What are you doing in this part of school? This is my area.
Kim	I'm going to my lesson.
Joanne	Then go back round by the science block.
Kim	I'll be late.
Joanne	You're not listening, are you?
Kim	I need to get past.

As Kim steps forward, Joanne pushes her against one of the other girls. The girl pushes Kim back. Joanne grabs Kim by the collar.

Joanne	I said, go back round by the science block. *(She pushes Kim to the ground.)* This is my territory. Nobody walks through this part of the school unless I say so.
Kim	I'll be late.
Girl 1	It's a no-go area for you.
Girl 2	So don't come round here.
Girl 1	Try and remember that for next time.
Joanne	Do you understand?
Kim	No, I don't.

As Kim attempts to get up, Joanne pushes her down.

Joanne	Get down. *(Girls 1 and 2 place their feet so that they are above Kim's left and right hands. Kim moves her hands. Joanne grabs Kim by the hair and pulls her head back.)* Put your fingers back! *(Kim obeys. Girls 1 and 2 place their feet over Kim's fingers. Joanne drips saliva onto Kim's back.)* Ah, look, someone's been spitting on her coat. *(Kim is yanked up.)* What are you going to do about it? *(Kim stares at Joanne.)* Answer me!
Kim	If you could really see what you looked like, you would be disgusted.
Joanne	*(Taking hold of Kim's chin)* You want to be careful what you say. We haven't finished with you yet. *(Kim breaks free.)*
Kim	Can't you leave me alone?
Joanne	Fight back. Show me you're not soft, then I'll leave you alone.
Girl 1	She hasn't got the guts.
Girl 2	You won't fight back, will you?
Kim	I won't reduce myself to your level.
Joanne	*(Pulling Kim forward by the hair)* You were saying?
Kim	Get off me! *(She manages to free herself and runs off.)*
Joanne	Coward!

Lights out.

Scene 3: Mr Wilson's office

Mr Wilson sits at his desk. Sarah and Kim stand. Kim holds a document.

Mr Wilson	Sit down Miss Lee. You're Kim's aunt, is that right?
Sarah	Kim's mother isn't well at the moment and she was happy for me to come.
Mr Wilson	I thought we had dealt with your little problem, Kim, but I see you've been taking some time off recently.
Sarah	Joanne Morton is still bullying Kim.

Mr Wilson	*(To Kim)* Is that why you've been staying off? We don't want you to worry about coming to school. We want all our pupils to feel safe here. Joanne Morton will be dealt with severely. You have my word on it.
Sarah	Kim's written something she wants you to look at.
Kim	They're ideas for dealing with bullying.
Mr Wilson	I'll read that later. Now I want you to leave this office feeling assured that we are going to do something about Joanne Morton.
Kim	Would you read my document before we go, Mr Wilson?
Sarah	I think it would help the situation.
Mr Wilson	Very well. *(He reads aloud.)* Dealing with bullying. One, there should be a place where pupils can report incidents of bullying. Two, notes should be kept on where and when bullying takes place. Three, persistent bullies should be watched and information collated. Severe sanctions should be applied to persistent bullies including isolation or exclusion. *(To Kim and Sarah)* Now most of this is more or less happening.
Kim	I'm just suggesting a way of formalising it. We could have a witness box.
Mr Wilson	And what is a witness box?
Kim	It's like a postbox that pupils use to report information on bullying.
Mr Wilson	That doesn't sound a bad idea. Of course, it will need someone to organise it. It could create a lot of extra work.
Kim	It's easier than reporting directly to a teacher.
Mr Wilson	You know you can report bullying to any teacher at any time and we do deal with bullies. Am I not going to deal with Joanne Morton? *(Reading)* Four, all parents should be informed that the school is making a stand against bullying and should be encouraged to help. Now that's sounds good but it can also generate the wrong kind of publicity for the school. Shall I read on?

Kim	There are only three more points.
Mr Wilson	*(He reads)* Five, teachers should look at the problem of bullying as subject matter for in their lessons, for example, PSHE, Drama or English. The more chance there is to discuss the problem, the more chance there is of dealing with it. Now that's a good idea but I think you'll find some teachers already look at bullying in their lessons.
Kim	Nobody has covered the topic with me, Mr Wilson.
Mr Wilson	It's not always easy to cover everything with every pupil. *(He continues reading.)* Six, teachers should supervise areas where it is known that bullying takes place. Seven, there should be counselling for the bullies, their supporters and the bully's parents. *(To Kim and Sarah)* Another two good ideas but there is the time factor again. You are expecting a lot from the teachers. They can't be everywhere and do everything.
Kim	I know it means extra work, but every day someone in school is bullied. If the victim were you or a member of staff, then you would deal with the situation. It would be the first priority because you know no one should abuse anyone else.
Mr Wilson	I promise you your problem will be solved.
Kim	It's not just me who is bullied.
Mr Wilson	Kim, I'm impressed by what you've written. It shows you're an intelligent girl. I am wondering whether you could use your intelligence to avoid the problem you've been having?
Kim	Two girls stood on my fingers whilst Joanne Morton spat on me. Do you want me to try and reason with them?
Mr Wilson	Maybe it's time to stand up to Joanne.
Kim	Do you mean fight back?
Mr Wilson	No, I mean bring a court action against Joanne Morton. That would end it.
Kim	I want the school to recognise there's a problem.
Mr Wilson	And we do! Miss Lee, thank you for coming. Kim, I'll take on board your ideas and I do expect to see you attending

school every day. We don't want to involve the educational welfare officer, do we?

Lights out on Mr Wilson, Kim and Sarah. Lights up on Mrs Marshall.

Mrs Marshall I was quite nervous about coming. This is the first time I've ever employed a solicitor this way. At this stage, I only want a letter giving my account of the incident, justification of my action and the fact that I would be prepared to take the case to court. These are the details…

Lights out on Mrs Marshall. She moves to another stage area. She meets with Kim. Lights up.

Kim Mum, I need to talk to you.

Mrs Marshall Not now, Kim. My head is spinning.

Lights out.

Scene 4: School

Kim is stage left. Suddenly from stage right, Joanne yells.

Joanne You! Get here! Bring her over to me! *(Kim turns but entering from stage left are Joanne's two friends. Joanne moves towards the centre. Kim is pushed towards her.)* I'll scratch your eyes out if you don't learn to keep your mouth shut. I'm on special report again thanks to you. He said he can't throw me out but he can make life unpleasant for me. Well the worse it gets for me, the worse it will get for you. *(To her friends)* Show her. *(Kim is pushed to the ground.)* I've a good mind to grind my bleeding heel into your face. Go on, squeal. You're going to need plenty of practice because this is the sort of treatment you'll be getting a lot of. *(To her friends)* Get her up. *(Joanne steps between Kim and one of the girls. Kim and Joanne face each other.)* Every day, I'll be after you, every day I'm going to find you and every day I'm going to make you wish you hadn't made this trouble for me.

Kim	What have I done to you?
Joanne	You reported me!
Kim	Because you keep picking on me. Can't you leave me alone?
Joanne	There's no chance of that.
Kim	*(Clenching her fist)* I could…
Joanne	You haven't got the guts.
Kim	I have.
Joanne	But you don't want to.
Kim	I can't keep taking this.
Joanne	*(Pushing her back)* Try it if you want to. *(Pushing her again)* Try it. *(One of the girls forces Kim's arm up her back.)* See what will happen. *(Kim is pushed to the ground and kicked by all the girls. Lights out on action. Lights up on Mrs Marshall.)*
Mrs Marshall	I'm relieved it's over. You've asked me if I would like to say something. Yes. I would. When I stopped that vicious assault in the supermarket, I was acting in the best interests of customers, employees, the company and, in particular, the victim of the assault. Unfortunately, the attacker's wrist was hurt. The last thing I would want to do is to hurt someone, even someone like that. Somerdales have been concerned that there might be a court action brought against them by the attacker and that there might be some adverse publicity, so, because of my commitment and my ability to do a good job, I have found the last couple of weeks unbearable. I just wonder how fair that is? I did not want to resort to a solicitor. I did not want to fight you, but unlike the victim of the attack, I have felt unsupported and have been forced to take action. Why should I be put in this situation when I haven't done anything wrong?

Lights out.

Scene 5: Mr Wilson's office

Kim *(Distressed)* I've been held down whilst Joanne Morton scraped her foot across my cheek. I've had my arm twisted and I've been kicked.

Mr Wilson She's gone too far this time. I put her on report and she has deliberately disobeyed me. I think you need to go home. Do you want me to ring your mother or father?

Kim Dad's working away and mum has a very important meeting at work today.

Mr Wilson Then what should we do with you? Perhaps you could sit in the library for half an hour and pull yourself together. Don't worry, Joanne Morton will be dealt with once and for all. We can't keep thugs like that in this school. After our conversation the other day, I've spoken with some of the staff. This will cheer you up… we're going to adopt some of your ideas. Next week during assemblies, staff are going to explain to the pupils about the witness box and I'm thinking about some of your other ideas. Go and clean yourself up. *(Kim begins to exit.)* I don't think you need to worry about Joanne Morton any more.

Lights out.

Scene 6: Sarah's home

Mrs Marshall They would not look at me directly. They all knew he was wrong. All that stress I went through, yet they were still suggesting that my letter was a threat to the company. *(Enter Kim.)* Kim? Why aren't you in school?

Kim I came to see Aunt Sarah.

Mrs Marshall You're early. Is it still this bullying?

Kim I was beaten up again today.

Mrs Marshall Oh Kim, why didn't you tell me how serious it was?

Kim I didn't want to worry you when you were losing your job.

Mrs Marshall	I haven't lost it. I've stood up to them. I've beaten their bully tactics. Now I'll see to you. First thing tomorrow morning, I'll go and see Mr Wilson.
Kim	It's finished with. I think Joanne Morton is going to be expelled.
Sarah	And about time.
Kim	Mr Wilson is using some of my ideas to prevent bullying in the school. At least that's come out of it.
Mrs Marshall	Are you sure you don't want me to go up to school?
Kim	It's all sorted, mum.
Mrs Marshall	Then we've both got something to celebrate. What about the three of us going out for a meal?

Lights out.

Scene 7: School grounds

Joanne	I've been waiting for you.
Kim	*(Looking round)* Where are your friends?
Joanne	Suspended.
Kim	What about you?
Joanne	Suspended and probably expelled after the governors' meeting.
Kim	Then you shouldn't be on school premises.
Joanne	Can you see this bruise? This is from my dad because he had to come to school this morning. He can't afford to miss the work when it's in. He's whacked me. So that's one I owe you.
Kim	It's not my fault your dad beats you.
Joanne	*(Menacing)* You didn't take any notice of my warnings did you? You had to go crying for help. *(She grabs Kim's hair, pulling Kim's head downwards then quickly jerking it up.)*

	I'm… I'm after you every day now. I can always get you, I can always…
Mr Wilson	*(Running in)* You can always what, Joanne Morton? You have been suspended until next Wednesday. Now I suggest you leave the premises quickly.
Joanne	*(Exiting)* Don't think that little coward has got away with it.
Mr Wilson	*(To Kim)* When Joanne returns, we'll be watching her very carefully. You won't need to worry.
Kim	I didn't want to fight.
Mr Wilson	I should have realised how serious all this was.
Kim	She thinks I'm a coward.
Mr Wilson	She's the coward, not you. She's been picking on someone who would not fight back. You are the one who's brave. You should be proud of yourself. Come on, I'll walk with you to your next lesson. *(They begin to exit and the lights begin to fade.)* I'm going to think about some of your ideas. You can come and talk to me about them tomorrow morning if you like. I think we've all learned something from this.

Lights out.

Worksheet on *Coward*

Questions

1 Why do you think Joanne is a bully?

....

2 Kim suggests a number of ways in which Mr Wilson can deal with bullying. Write down three of these suggestions:

a ....

....

b ....

....

c ....

....

3 Which suggestions do you think are the best and why?

....

....

4 Kim tells Joanne that she does not want to reduce herself to her level. What does she mean by this?

....

5 Does it make sense that Kim does not want to fight back? Give a reason for your answer.

....

6 What does Kim mean by a 'witness box'?

....

7 Who is the coward of the play? Think very carefully about your answer.

....

....

8 What are the similarities and differences between what happens to Kim and her mother?

....

....

....

9 At the end of the play, Mr Wilson says, "we've all learned something." What do you think he has learned?

....

Extension work

1 Using Kim's suggestions for dealing with bullying as a basis, write out a notice that would explain to pupils in a school the bullying policy.

2 Find out the meaning of:
- scapegoat
- collate.

Classroom improvisation

Improvise or prepare for presentation the following:

a Mr Wilson speaking to Joanne or Joanne's father.

b A teacher speaking to Joanne's friends and explaining why they are wrong to support her.

Classroom Bullies

The play is suitable for:

- assembly presentation performances
- workshop performances
- open evening performances
- classroom reading for KS3.

Cast list

Teacher
Darren
Tahreem
Natalia
Andrea
Imran
Joseph
Sarah
Sharon
Daniel
Veronica
Renée
Joanne
Jenny
Robbie
Pupils 1-6
Andrew

Production notes

Names can be changed to pupils' real names if required. All parts can be amended to male or female. Pupils 1 to 6 can be played by the 'named' pupils if necessary. With relatively few adjustments, the play can be presented by a small group or a full class.

Lighting is uncomplicated: switch on at the beginning and switch off at the end. The play would benefit from playing some music at the beginning and ending.

The set is simple – a drama space. The play is suitable for presenting in the round, open end or traverse staging.

Properties are two chairs and a sheet of paper.

The running time is approximately 20 minutes.

Classroom Bullies

———— o ————

Pupils are waiting for the teacher in the drama area. The teacher enters.

Teacher   I've sorted out the information from our last lesson. Come on, gather round me. *(The pupils sit on the floor in front of the teacher.)* If you remember, I asked you to write down the names of the pupils you considered to be the biggest bullies in this class. *(Looking at a piece of paper)* What is interesting is that altogether you've identified six pupils who bully. So this, for me, seems to justify a look at bullying. As we explore the topic, those of you who have engaged in bullying at any time will realise the problems it causes and the opinion people have of you when you do it. The one name at the top of the list I want to keep secret. That person has been voted a bully by everyone. Hopefully, they will learn the most. OK, everyone into a space. *(The pupils stand in a space.)* Breathe in, breathe out… and again, breathe in, and out. Find a partner. Has everyone got a partner?

Darren   Miss, I haven't.

Teacher   Join up with another two. *(To the class)* Last time we discussed why people bully. What did we find out?

Darren   They bully for attention, Miss.

Tahreem   We also looked at how they bully.

Teacher   That's right. I want a freeze time which shows one person physically bullying another. Ten seconds. 10, 9, 8, 7… *(As the teacher counts backwards from 10, the pupils quickly form the freeze-frames. The teacher looks at the frames.)* Renée, don't hold Dawn's throat so tightly. Imran, don't grab Joseph there. OK… relax everyone.

Tahreem   Miss, sometimes they do it without hitting anybody. They just threaten them.

Teacher   That's right, verbal bullying. We talked about that last time. In a freeze-frame, show me an example of verbal bullying. *(Again, as the teacher counts backwards from 10, the pupils quickly form freeze-frames. The teacher looks at the frames.)* No Sharon, sticking your tongue out isn't bullying, it's rude. Put it away please. *(The pupils laugh.)* Gather round me. *(Again, the pupils sit on the floor in front of the teacher.)* I'm going to tell you why I started this topic. Andrew, listen to what I'm going to say please. My eldest son was bullied at his school. It caused him a lot of distress. When I eventually found out about it, words came into my head, words which I felt described the bully. Can you think of words that describe a bully?

Darren	Mean.
Tahreem	Vicious.
Natalia	Selfish.
Andrea	Thoughtless.
Imran	Nasty.
Joseph	Horrible.
Sarah	Coward.
Sharon	Cruel.
Daniel	Unintelligent.
Veronica	Ignorant.
Renée	Aggressive.
Joanne	Threatening.
Jenny	Arrogant.
Robbie	Violent.
Pupil 1	Sly.
Pupil 2	Jealous.
Pupil 3	Bighead.
Pupil 4	Show-off.
Pupil 5	Blackmailer.
Pupil 6	Pathetic.
Teacher	What about words that describe how the victim feels?
Darren	What's a victim, Miss?
Teacher	All those big words and Darren asks me the meaning of the word 'victim'.
Natalia	The person who is bullied.
Teacher	That's right. As you think of a word, call it out, then go and sit in a space.

Darren	Upset.
Tahreem	Worried.
Natalia	Angry.
Andrea	Scared.
Imran	Helpless.
Joseph	Hurt.
Sarah	Insecure.
Sharon	Depressed.
Daniel	Embarrassed.
Veronica	Humiliated.
Renée	Inferior.
Joanne	Terrified.
Jenny	Tormented.
Robbie	Lonely.
Pupil 1	Ashamed.
Pupil 2	Weak.
Pupil 3	Intimidated.
Pupil 4	Nervous.
Pupil 5	Sad.
Pupil 6	Isolated.
Teacher	OK. Find a different partner. This time, one of you will be in role as someone on their way to see the Headteacher. You've been bullying and you're in trouble. On the way, you meet a friend. Your partner can take on that role. Decide who's going to be who. *(Pupils find a partner. As Joseph and Imran pair up, Andrew pulls Joseph away. Imran suggests a group of three.)* Positions and start. *(Pupils role-play the exercise.)*
Teacher	*(After a short while)* Let's listen in here. *(Apart from the nominated pupils, the others stop and watch.)*

Natalia	He'll only tell me off or put me in detention.
Andrea	That little lad you were pushing about is soft. It serves him right.
Natalia	Next time, I'll take his dinner money.
Teacher	Wait a minute, shouldn't the bully be worried that she's in trouble?
Imran	Some of them don't care, Miss.
Teacher	Then let's see what happens when they get to the Headteacher. This time, Sharon, you be the bully and Sarah, you be the Headteacher. Use two chairs.

The pupils begin to act out the roles.

Sarah	Now Sharon, a little bird tells me you've been bullying some of the children in your class. Do you think that's a very nice thing to do?
Sharon	No, Miss.
Sarah	Right, off you go and don't do it again.
Teacher	You weren't really in the role were you, Sarah?
Sarah	How's that, Miss?
Teacher	That was a rather brief conversation and you were picking at your nose. Teachers don't do things like that.
Sarah	Mr Simons does.
Teacher	I'm sure he doesn't.
Sarah	He does and he wipes it...
Teacher	*(Interrupting)* Thank you, Sarah. I think we're getting sidetracked. Let's go back to the business of bullying. *(To the class)* Do you think the Headteacher's talk here would stop the bullying?
Imran	No, Miss, Sharon would keep on bullying.
Andrea	I think the Headteacher should punish her.
Natalia	Or make her realise how horrible she is.

Teacher	How would the Headteacher do that?
Tahreem	Use the words.
Imran	What words?
Jenny	Our words. Tell them what people think about them.
Darren	They're mean.
Tahreem	Vicious.
Natalia	Selfish.
Andrea	Thoughtless.
Imran	Nasty.
Joseph	Horrible.
Sarah	Coward.
Sharon	Cruel.
Darren	Unintelligent.
Veronica	Ignorant.
Renée	Aggressive.
Joanne	Threatening.
Jenny	Arrogant.
Robbie	Violent.
Pupil 1	Sly.
Pupil 2	Jealous.
Pupil 3	Bighead.
Pupil 4	Show-off.
Pupil 5	Blackmailer.
Pupil 6	Pathetic.
Imran	Can we do the improvisation, Miss?
Teacher	Yes, if you want to. *(Imran drags Joseph to centre stage. They begin their role-play.)*
Imran	Why have I asked you to come to my office, Joseph?

Joseph	I don't know, Sir.
Imran	Well, I'll tell you. You're a bully. Other children have been complaining about you. And would you like to know what they say about you?
Joseph	*(Ashamed)* No, Sir.
Imran	Well, you can listen anyway. They say you're a coward, a bighead, you're selfish, vicious, thoughtless, arrogant, jealous and pathetic.
Teacher	*(Stopping the role-play)* That's good because the bully is being told exactly what the other children think about him. *(To Imran)* Erm, wasn't Andrew in your group?
Andrew	I didn't want to do it, Miss. *(The teacher sighs.)*
Teacher	*(To the class)* If you remember, in last week's lesson we established that bullies bully for attention... they want people to notice them.
Tahreem	They hope people think they're tough.
Teacher	All the more reason to point out what people really think.
Imran	It doesn't stop them bullying.
Teacher	So what should we do about it?
Sharon	Tell their parents.
Teacher	That's right. Let's try that in role. In twos again. One of you will be the Headteacher, the other the parent of the bully. *(To Andrew)* Will you join in this time, Andrew?
Andrew	Yes, Miss.
Teacher	Perhaps Imran will sit this one out. Is everyone ready? Positions and start. *(In role, the pupils act out the encounter.)* Stop. Let's listen into Daniel and Veronica. *(Daniel and Veronica begin acting again. They use the two chairs.)*
Daniel	Well Miss Thompson, I'm very worried about the situation. I had no idea he was like that. Fancy him making children scared and upset.
Veronica	Yes, it's unfair on the victims, isn't it?

Daniel	I feel ashamed. He'll be punished.
Veronica	What about pointing out to him what the other children think about him and how he's made some of them feel.
Teacher	*(Interrupting)* Very good.
Renée	Miss, sometimes pupils don't always tell the teachers.
Teacher	Who do they tell?
Renée	Nobody, they're too scared.
Teacher	What if somone had got to the stage where they couldn't take the bullying any longer and they really did want to tell someone? Jenny, you and Robbie improvise that for us. *(Daniel and Veronica vacate the chairs. Robbie sits down. Jenny stands.)*
Jenny	What's wrong, Robbie?
Robbie	Nothing, Miss.
Jenny	I can see something is wrong. Are you in trouble?
Robbie	No, Miss. (**Nervous but speaking eventually**) Jason Smithson picks on me every day. I'm just fed up with it. And it's no good saying hit him back. He's twice my size. Every time he passes me on the corridor, he pokes me in the ribs. Any time I'm in a line for something, he pushes me out of the way. He jumped on me in the yard. It's all the time, Miss. I've had enough.
Jenny	We'll try to sort it out.
Robbie	Nobody will be able to sort it out. He'll always do it. If he doesn't stop, I'm not coming to school again.
Teacher	*(Interrupting the role-play)* Is this fair on Robbie? He's in such a state that he's scared to come to school. But that's what bullying does. Remember the list you made? There were six names on it. If you take part in bullying, you are making people feel like Robbie in that last piece of drama.
Renée	Miss, Andrew's laughing.

Joanne	That's because he's a bully. His name's on the list. He's like all bullies, he likes it when people are hurt, that's why they do it.
Tahreem	Or for attention.
Andrew	Shut up or you'll get it afterwards.
Teacher	Well I had hoped I was beginning to get you to think about bullying in a sensible way, but it seems to be a waste of time with you, Andrew.
Andrew	*(Adamantly)* I don't bully people.
Others	Yes you do.
Teacher	You were doing it before. I've been watching you in the role-plays. You're not taking the lesson seriously.
Andrew	I don't have to. Anyway, it's not real. They're only plays. I don't need to learn about them.
Teacher	That's where you're wrong. You, more than anyone else in this class, needs to learn! It's because of people like you I'm doing the lesson. You're top of this list! The one everyone here thinks is a bully.
Andrew	Well, they're wrong.
Teacher	*(Earnestly)* Please, please Andrew, learn from this topic.
Andrew	*(Hard-faced)* Can I go to the toilet?
Sarah	Don't let him go, Miss.
Andrew	Just you wait.
Teacher	*(Matter of fact)* Andrew, you can go to the toilet. *(As Andrew exits, the teacher indicates that the pupils should gather round her.)* We're going to try a special role-play. Hopefully, it will make Andrew realise how wrong it is to be a bully. I'm going to set you a series of tasks but I'm also going to ask you to do something else. When Andrew returns, I don't want anyone to speak to him. That's the special role-play. You have to completely ignore him until I tell you otherwise.
Renée	What if he stands next to me?

Teacher	Move away.
Joanne	That's what we learned in the first lesson. If everyone ignores the bully, he's got no one to show off to.
Teacher	I'm hoping he'll learn more than that. Right, everyone in pairs. One of you is the parent of a bully, your partner is the parent of the child who has been bullied. This parent calls on the bully's parents to discuss the problem. Are you ready to start? Don't forget, no one must speak to Andrew.
Robbie	What if he makes us?
Imran	You must make sure he doesn't. *(Andrew enters.)*
Teacher	You're just in time Andrew. They've all got a partner but you can join in with any pair. Go on Andrew. *(Andrew approaches the pupils. The first pair turn their backs on him, the next pair move away from him.)* Positions and start. *(The pupils begin the role-play.)* Come on Andrew, find yourself some friends to work with. They'll explain the work to you. *(Every time Andrew approaches pupils, they move away or ignore him. He takes hold of Imran by the arm. Imran shrugs him off and moves with his partner near the teacher.)* OK, stop. That was very good. You didn't join in Andrew.
Andrew	Nobody would let me.
Teacher	*(Firmly)* You didn't try hard enough. *(To the class)* Let's try another exercise.
Joseph	Are we still in our special role?
Darren	Of course we are. *(A squeal of delight is heard from Sharon.)*
Teacher	This time Tahreem will give the instructions.
Tahreem	Stay with your partner. One of you is the bully. One of your parents has been to see the Headteacher. When you arrive home, your parent is waiting to see you.
Teacher	Well done, Tahreem. Right, Andrew, form a threesome. *(Whenever Andrew approaches a pair, they move away.)* Come on Andrew, get sorted out.

Andrew	Miss, nobody will work with me.
Teacher	*(Acting annoyed)* Of course they will. You're not making an attempt to get into a group. Stand over there and watch. Right everyone, positions and start. *(The pupils begin. Eventually the teacher stops the role-play.)* Let's listen to Natalia and Andrea.
Natalia	I'll tell you, it's because you're selfish, ignorant, cruel and more than anything else, you're a coward. You only pick on people who won't fight back. I hope you feel proud of yourself because I feel totally ashamed!
Teacher	*(Interrupting)* Marvellous, well done Natalia. *(To the class)* I want you to get into small groups of four or five and this time Andrew make sure you find a group.
Andrew	*(Worried)* What if nobody will work with me?
Teacher	*(Shouting)* Go and find a group! *(As the pupils make their groups, Andrew is left by himself.)*
Teacher	*(To the class)* What does injustice mean?
Veronica	When it's not fair.
Joseph	When you're punished for something you haven't done.
Sharon	Or just for no reason.
Teacher	I want you to prepare an improvisation that shows the rest of the class an example of injustice.
Andrew	Miss, I can't get in a group.
Teacher	If you don't find a group Andrew, you'll be punished.
Andrew	Miss, that's injustice.
Teacher	*(Snapping back)* No it isn't. It's your inability to organise yourself. *(The groups sit down and begin talking. Andrew goes from group to group but no one will let him join in. Head bowed, he stands still.)* Right, everyone. Out of the special role. *(The pupils laugh. Andrew looks sad and bewildered.)*
Daniel	Miss said we weren't to talk to you.

Teacher	It was unjust, wasn't it Andrew? *(Andrew bows his head.)* And every time you bully, that's what you're being. How did it feel to be the one who was upset, worried and embarrassed? Cowards don't like it when it's their turn to be intimidated. *(Andrew's fingers rub at his eyes. His head is still bowed.)*

Teacher	*(Intimidating)* So how does it feel now?
Jenny	He's upset, Miss.
Teacher	I can see that. Now he knows what it's like to be the victim. It's a different story now. *(Andrew runs off.)*
Andrea	Shall I go after him, Miss?
Teacher	No. Leave him to think.
Tahreem	I don't think we needed to make him cry.

Darren	We didn't, it was Miss.
Tahreem	We played along with the game.
Joseph	But it wasn't our idea.
Teacher	If he's learned a lesson it's all been worth it.
Tahreem	But you were a bully as well.
Andrea	I think we were mean.
Natalia	And cruel.
Sharon	And all those other words. It wasn't fair.
Teacher	It's time to get changed now. Off you go.
Tahreem	End of the lesson, Miss.
Teacher	New topic next week, I think.

Worksheet on *Classroom Bullies*

Questions

1 Write down five of the words the pupils use to describe how a victim feels.

....

....

2 Write down five of the words the pupils use to describe a bully.

....

....

3 Why did the teacher start the bullying project?

....

4 Why did the teacher think that Sarah was not really in role?

....

5 What is the reason Andrew gives for not taking the lesson seriously?

....

6 What does 'injustice' mean?

....

7 What was the special role-play?

....

8 Who is the bully in the play? Try to justify your answer.

....

....

....

Happy Waiting Day

The play is suitable for:

- drama/performing arts examination performances
- workshop presentations
- classroom reading for KS4.

Cast list

Eileen
John
Jane
David
Gran

Production notes

The play will benefit from playing appropriate music at the ending and at the beginning prior to the singing of *Happy Birthday*.

Lighting is simple: switch on at the beginning and off at the end.

Properties are:

* a stool
* a bottle of champagne
* glasses
* a birthday cake with candles.

The running time is approximately ten minutes.

Happy Waiting Day

———— o ————

A stool is centre stage. Strains of 'Happy Birthday' are heard. The singers are the family. Gran walks to the stool and sits down. From the four corners of the acting area, the family enter one at a time. They stand next to Gran. They face downstage. At times, the family will speak to what appears to be a camera. This cannot be seen.

Eileen	Happy birthday, mum. You look very nice.
John	Happy birthday, mum. Try to enjoy some of it.
Jane	Happy birthday, gran. I know you will be strong.
David	Happy birthday, gran. I'm sorry.
Eileen	You're a very special person.
David	How do you feel, gran?
Eileen	She feels good… don't you, mum?
Jane	We should start the recording.
Eileen	You keep thinking good memories, mum.
Gran	I can't think, I can't think straight. Don't start the recording for the moment. Give me time to get ready. I want to be clear.
Jane	It could be any time.
Eileen	They always knock. It's never the buzzer or the bell. Three loud thuds.
John	Almost mechanical.
Jane	That's one of the rules.
John	I suppose it has to be.
Eileen	It marks the door.

Jane	It gives you a warning.
David	What time will it be?
Jane	They never tell you the time. It's another rule. We should begin the recording. We're wasting time.
Eileen	I'll speak first. Don't record yet. Let me try this out.
Jane	Mother, you should have been ready.
Eileen	Do you think it's that easy? How can I be ready?
Jane	Speak.
Eileen	My mother was born 75 years ago. She married Joseph Eastwood when they were both 18. Some people said she was too young, but she stayed married for 45 years. She has one daughter, that's me. She came to stay with us when dad passed away. I knew about this day then but I hoped we would never have to face it. *(To Gran)* That's too factual. It doesn't sound as if there's any sort of relationship. You were a good mother. I hope in the last two years I've looked after you. *(She gathers strength.)* Why does this have to happen? Why is there a rule that when a person is 75 their time is up?
Jane	It balances the population.
Eileen	A maximum life span of 75 years and a maximum of two children. Maxi… Maxi… mum. It doesn't make much sense that word, does it?
Jane	It prevents housing problems, traffic problems, unemployment, and poverty.
Eileen	Why do you tell me the arguments?
Jane	No urine sheets, no forgetfulness, deceasing with dignity and we remember her before any failings. I want that.
Eileen	For me or for yourself?
Jane	For both of us, it's the right way.
Eileen	Won't it hurt you when it's my turn? I don't know how to let my mother go.
Jane	You don't have to. Someone will do it for you.

Eileen	How can you be so cold?
Jane	We haven't begun the recording. If we start now, it gives us more to edit from later. We might miss something. I'll set it going. We'll begin with dad; perhaps we can end with you, mum. It will give you more time to think.
Eileen	It's not me who needs the time.
Jane	Are you ready, dad?

Jane presses a handheld control panel to begin the recording. John speaks.

John	I thought when she came, she would cause problems to our lifestyle. But I have to admit, she's fitted in. It's been no trouble. I will be sorry to see her go. I voted for this in the referendum, Eileen didn't. My father was dead, I never knew my mother. How can you vote for something like that? I hadn't really anticipated this day.
David	I want the rule changed. I want gran to stay.
Jane	You can't change the rule.
David	I'm dreading that knock.
Jane	There will be three.
John	Let's open a bottle of champagne and bring in the birthday cake. Make the most of the last few hours. What else can we do? I mean, what else should we be doing? Come with me, mum. We'll bring your cake together.
Gran	I can't, I can't move.
Eileen	I'll help you.
Gran	I'll stay here. I'll wait. Eileen will go with you.
Eileen	Is that what you want, mum?
Gran	Yes.
Jane	Gran should be on the recording all the time.

John and Eileen exit.

David	I remember when you used to take us to the open spaces,

gran, looking at the trees and all the grass. It was lovely. It was warm. I love you gran. I never ever wanted this day.

Gran	Look after your mum and dad.
David	I will. I'll always do it.
Jane	We have rules to help us.
Gran	I want David to tell me what else he remembers.
David	Once we flew to a small Spanish village. It was beautiful with white buildings. There was a donkey. How old was I then?
Gran	You were five. Do you remember riding the donkey? It clattered up that steep street. It always used to slip and you always screamed.
David	Did Jane ride the donkey?
Gran	She didn't scream.
Jane	I don't remember.
David	We ate outside every night, but after the meal one night it became cold all of a sudden. I remember you shivering. The warmth just disappeared.
Gran	The end of the day. That's the whole memory.
David	*(Taking hold of Gran's hands)* Your hands are cold. Now you're shivering. *(John and Eileen enter with champagne, glasses and the cake.)*
John	What should we drink a toast to? What do you want to remember?
Jane	Today's a celebration. We celebrate gran's 75 years. You know that's what we should be doing.
Eileen	You need feelings to celebrate.
John	*(Pouring champagne for Gran)* Here, mum, take this glass. Jane will pour the rest. You make the toast, Eileen.
Eileen	*(Upset)* I can't.
Jane	*(Handing her mother a glass of champagne)* Gran would really like to hear you say nice things.

Eileen	*(Upset and finding it difficult to speak)* I can't speak.
Jane	That's not fair on gran.
Eileen	Then you say something! Use it as a practice for when it's my turn! Why don't they knock? Why don't they do it now? I can't stand the waiting. *(She pauses, she gathers herself.)* I'm sorry, I'm taking away your time.
Gran	The time doesn't matter. They'll be here when they're here.
Jane	I'll make the toast, we're supposed to do. *(Lifting her glass)* To the best of gran's memories. Tell us what you remember, gran.
Gran	I have some good memories. I remember when your mother was born. I remember holding her and waiting for your grandad. I remember her breath. I remember taking her to the dentists. She screamed so loud, a little girl in the waiting room ran out. I remember her standing in her first school uniform. She said she wanted to learn. She said she wanted to go but she cried so hard in the playground that as I walked to the car I couldn't turn round. When her examination results came through, we cried together and very soon she met you, John. Then the children, David and Jane. Like your mother, you both wanted to learn at school, but you were different… different to each other… that's not unusual for a brother and a sister. Jane always chose research studies, sciences, mathematics, logic, but David chose sensitivity development. You've become more and more different. Now you're both dealing with the world in your own way. I'm trying to make myself as prepared as I can but the longer I wait, the harder it is to keep my composure.
Jane	They'll be here soon.
Eileen	She doesn't want to hear that.
Jane	I'll make my testimony. Thank you gran. You've helped in our home. You contributed to my language development. You are over-emotional but people are different and I accept that. I know you think I'm callous but it's only because I understand the future. It's necessary to control everything and that control begins with our emotions. In

this end time, there is a lot of good to celebrate. You have your family with you. You've reached the age; some people die before it. You're fit, you're well and you've avoided physical and mental deterioration. We can celebrate your achievements. I'll light the candles.

Gran   When I blow out the candles, will I see darkness?

Jane   You can't see darkness.

Gran   Then what will I see?

David   You'll see us, your future.

Gran   These candles are my past.

John   They're your memories.

Eileen   And achievements.

David   Keep seeing us, gran.

Gran   I don't want to see the darkness.

Three knocks are heard. There is a pause as they all look at each other.

Eileen	I didn't make my testimony.
John	She knows how you feel.
Eileen	I know how she feels. There will be a day like this for me.
David	I'll be there for you mum.
Eileen	And Jane?
Gran	Jane will be efficient.
Jane	It's time.
Gran	You must look ahead. Don't turn round. When you replay the recording, there shouldn't be any tears. Keep looking ahead. I don't want anyone to say anything. Keep looking ahead.
Eileen	Touch my face before you leave.
Gran	Be like Jane.
Jane	Keep looking ahead.

Gran begins to exit.

Eileen	Keep looking ahead until it's my turn.
Gran	Keep looking ahead.

She exits. Fade to blackout.

Worksheet on *Happy Waiting Day*

What are Jane's arguments for the maximum life span of 75 years?

....

....

....

....

....

Compare the characters of Jane and David.

....

....

....

....

....

....

....

What is your opinion of 'compulsory euthanasia' at 75?

....

....

....

....

....

....

The Secret

Suitable for:

- classroom/drama performances
- workshop presentations
- use as part of a series of sketches
- open evening performances
- classroom reading for KS3.

Cast list

Emma
Mary

Production notes

The play can be quite easily learned and presented in the classroom or drama area. The pauses are important and the actors should still be acting during these times. Emma and Mary are probably quite young although if the line "Me mum says I've got to stay here" is replaced by "I'm staying here", you could imagine the play being about two older ladies. Try it various ways. Try it with accents; as young girls; as older ladies; one drunk, one sober; one excited, one very calm; one irritated, one very happy. See what you can come up with.

The running time is approximately five minutes.

The Secret

Lights up. Mary should be far stage left. Emma should be far stage right. If possible, there should be a single profile spot on Emma and a follow spot on Mary.

Mary   Emma! Emma!

Emma   What?

Mary   *(Loudly)* I'll tell you a secret!

Emma   What secret?

Mary   Come here.

Emma	I can't. Me mum says I've got to stay here.
Mary	Well I'm not coming over there. It's my secret.
Emma	If you want to tell me, you'll have to come here.
Mary	No, you come here.
Emma	If you want to tell me, you'll have to come here.
Mary	No, you come here.
Emma	I've just told you, me mum says I've got to stay here.

Pause.

Mary	It's a really good secret.
Emma	Well, tell me from there.
Mary	I can't, I have to whisper it.
Emma	Well whisper it from there.
Mary	You won't be able to hear if I whisper from here.
Emma	I will if you whisper loudly.

Pause.

Mary	I'll meet you halfway.
Emma	You come halfway first.

Mary moves halfway.

Mary	I'm halfway. Come on.
Emma	I told you before, me mum says I've got to stay here.
Mary	But I've come halfway!
Emma	Well why don't you come halfway again, then I might be able to hear you whisper.
Mary	If I come halfway again, will you come halfway?
Emma	You come first.
Mary	It's my secret.

Emma   *(More forcefully)* You come first.

Mary moves.

Mary   I've come halfway again! Come on!

Emma   I've told you before, me mum says I've got to stay here.

Mary   Look, I'll come halfway again, but this is the last time.

Emma   Okay.

Mary moves.

Mary   Come on.

Emma   Try whispering from there.

Mary   *(Annoyed)* Do you want to hear this secret?

Emma   Yes. Whisper from there. I'll probably be able to hear you now.

Mary   Oh… alright. Well last week…

Mary whispers.

Emma   Oh! I already knew that.

Snap blackout.

My Mother Says

Suitable for:

- performing in classroom/drama area
- use as part of a series of sketches
- classroom reading for KS3/4.

Cast list

A boy

Production notes

My Mother Says is a fun play, easy to remember, and easy to perform.

Perhaps you could write or act out your own short, short play that involves one person and only one or two lines.

Think about the following:

- a fisherman
- someone who is tired
- someone who forgets where they are
- someone who forgets what they are going to say
- someone who is over-confident
- someone with something new
- someone with exciting news.

The running time is approximately one minute.

My Mother Says

———— ○ ————

Enter a boy.

He looks mindlessly at the audience, then appears to be thinking. He opens his mouth as if he is going to speak, closes it, looks puzzled then exits.

He re-enters.

He looks mindlessly at the audience again, turns his head to the right, opens his mouth and stares as if mesmerised.

Again he looks at the audience. He finally speaks.

Boy   My mother says… *(pause)* I'm dozy.

He opens his mouth and stares for a few seconds.

Boy   I don't know why.

He exits.

Blank music/sound effects sheet

Page	Details	Link music/sound effects

Blank lighting cue sheet

Page	Cue	Lighting